2(

D1094278

As I Walked Out One Evening

AS I WALKED OUT ONE EVENING

A Book of Ballads

Selected by HELEN PLOTZ

GREENWILLOW BOOKS
A Division of William Morrow & Company, Inc.
New York

Library of Congress Cataloging in Publication Data
Main entry under title: As I walked out one evening.
Summary: A collection of old and modern ballads
arranged under six headings: magic and miracles,
narratives, broadsides and satires, war, work, and love.
1. Ballads, English—Texts. 2. Ballads, American—Texts.
[1. Ballads, English. 2. Ballads, American] I.
Plotz, Helen.
PR1181.A75 821'.04 76-10306
ISBN 0-688-80054-8
ISBN 0-688-84054-X lib. bdg.

To the memory of Milton
And to our children
〰 *Elizabeth and Richard*
〰 *Paul and Judith*
〰 *Sarah and Roy*
〰 *John*

20953

SONG'S ETERNITY

What is song's eternity?
   Come and see.
Can it noise and bustle be?
   Come and see.
Praises sung or praises said
   Can it be?
Wait awhile and these are dead—
   Sigh, sigh;
Be they high or lowly bred
   They die.

What is song's eternity?
   Come and see.
Melodies of earth and sky
   Here they be.
Song once sung to Adam's ears
   Can it be?
Ballads of six thousand years
   Thrive, thrive;
Songs awakened with the spheres
   Alive.

Mighty songs that miss decay,
   What are they?
Crowds and cities pass away
   Like a day.
Books are writ and books are read;
   What are they?
Years will lay them with the dead—
   Sigh, sigh;
Trifles unto nothing wed,
   They die.

Dreamers, list the honey-bee;
    Mark the tree
Where the bluecap, "tootle tee,"
    Sings a glee
Sung to Adam and to Eve—
    Here they be.
When floods covered every bough,
    Noah's ark
Heard that ballad singing now;
    Hark, hark,

"Tootle tootle tootle tee"—
    Can it be
Pride and fame must shadows be?
    Come and see—
Every season owns her own;
    Bird and bee
Sing creation's music on;
    Nature's glee
Is in every mood and tone
    Eternity.

The eternity of song
    Liveth here;
Nature's universal tongue
    Singeth here
Songs I've heard and felt and seen
    Everywhere;
Songs like the grass are evergreen:
    The giver
Said "Live and be"—and they have been,
    For ever.

JOHN CLARE

x

INTRODUCTION

Ballads have been praised and scorned, loved and feared for hundreds of years. They have never been defined—quite. Most scholars agree that a ballad tells a story. Sometimes though, a ballad arises from an unrecorded but presumably well-known story. There are songs of love and of mourning, as well as political diatribes which are often classified as ballads. The old ballads were meant to be sung and should not be separated from their music, yet our greatest ballad students, Bishop Thomas Percy, Sir Walter Scott and Francis James Child, have published magnificent collections without the accompanying tunes.

There is a recognizable rhythm and rhyme scheme that prevails in most traditional and many modern ballads. The rhythm is compelling, the rhyme no less so. Ballads almost always have refrains and these refrains have made them easier to memorize, to sing and to recite.

As to their origins, there was a time when the folk theory prevailed. Ballads were supposed to have arisen when the "folk" gathered around and recalled legends or sang of incidents among the high or the lowly. Today few scholars accept this hypothesis. Most believe that long-forgotten poets composed the ballads and that their variants can be accounted for by their having been sung by many minstrels and passed on from generation to generation as nursery rhymes have been. I am convinced that every ballad is the creation, to quote James Weldon Johnson's wonderful phrase, of "an unknown bard of long ago."

This is not to discount the importance of oral tradition. The ballads of our English-speaking world were sung and in some places are still being sung by those who learned them from the elders of their families or communities. It is true that the invention of printing changed the nature of balladry in ways sometimes unforeseen. One might indeed say that William Caxton's first printed work in 1477 began a process that still goes on. Fortunately for us there have been and still are devoted lovers of the ballad who listen to the singers and who patiently transcribe the songs they hear in lonely cottages, in mining camps, in the streets of the cities and in the haunts of seamen and of cowboys.

Sir Walter Scott showed the printed texts of the old ballads to the mother of a now-forgotten Scottish poet, James Hogg, The Ettrick Shepherd. She had sung many ballads for Scott, but she said: "There was never ane o' ma songs prentit till ye prentit them yoursel' and ye hae spoilt them aw thegither. They were made for singing and no for reading, but ye hae broken the charm now and they'll never be sung mair. And the warst thing o' a', they're nouther richt spell'd nor richt setten down."

Before Scott published *Minstrelsy of the Scottish Border* in 1802, Bishop Thomas Percy had rescued a manuscript collection of poetry from a housemaid about to light a fire with it. (Such rescues have occurred more than once in the history of English literature.) Percy's *Reliques of Ancient English Poetry*, published in 1765, was the first serious attempt to gather together the old songs that had been sung for hundreds of years.

There were two notable forgeries, if they were forgeries, during the years immediately following the publication of the *Reliques*. Thomas Chatterton, "the marvelous boy" as

Wordsworth called him, had written ballads and epics which he claimed to have found in old manuscripts, and James Macpherson had translated from the Gaelic, or so he said, the poems of Ossian. The time had come for Scott, for Wordsworth and for Coleridge. Balladry dominated the movement which we now call the Romantic Revival. At the end of the nineteenth century, a professor at Harvard, Francis James Child, published *English and Scottish Popular Ballads*, a masterpiece of scholarship, now the definitive and glorious collection.

Ballads are elemental, stark, outspoken. Words are simple, direct, few. Ballads tell of faithfulness and faithlessness, of revenge, jealousy and murder, of transcending love and blinding hate. The story is stripped to the bare bone—there is no probing, no explanation. Often we must guess at what went before and this very spareness gives tremendous force to the climax.

The most striking example of this is "Edward, Edward" whose final stanza carries within itself a story of passionate hatred and pure evil. Two ballads that are outwardly similar tell stories that are directly opposite in their effects. "The Twa Corbies" and "The Three Ravens" each tell of a knight dead on the battlefield and of his lady. As in "Edward, Edward," the last stanzas convey the "zero at the bone."

Often traditional ballads tell of supernatural happenings. Stories of the changeling child, the demon lover, the young man enticed by the queen of Elfland, the returning dead, occur again and again in American as well as in English, Scottish and Irish ballads.

Rarely, ballads are comic. And, perhaps characteristically, many comic ballads are American. One can easily imagine "Clementine" as a tragic story, but indomitable pioneer humor has made it extremely funny.

Although I have said that I believe that all ballads have authors, I have been speaking of them, as indeed others do, as if they did not. The many versions of the old ballads reflect changing scenes and times. This is most striking in the American versions of traditional ballads. I have chosen some to juxtapose with the originals so that we can see those changes.

With the invention of printing came the broadside ballad. Most often it told of a political happening; occasionally a murder or other sensational event was described. In *The Winter's Tale* Shakespeare introduces Autolycus, the ballad seller, one of whose listeners says:

CLOWN. What hast here? Ballads?

MOPSA. Pray now, buy some. I love a ballad in print, o' life, for then we are sure they are true.

AUTOLYCUS. Here's one to a very doleful tune, how a usurer's wife was brought to bed of twenty money-bags at a burden, and how she long'd to eat adders' heads and toads carbonado'd.

MOPSA. Is it true, think you?

AUTOLYCUS. Very true, and but a month old.

DORCAS. Bless me from marrying a usurer!

AUTOLYCUS. Here's the midwife's name to't, one Mistress Taleporter, and five or six honest wives that were present. Why should I carry lies abroad?

MOPSA. Pray you now, buy it.

The broadside still exists. "Folk" singers now tell of current events, using the ballad as a newspaper. This was the function of the broadside before newspapers existed and during the time when newspapers were not so widely circulated and were too expensive for most people. The ballads were tacked up on tavern walls, hawked through the streets, and sung wherever people gathered together.

There have been times when these ballads have had tremendous power. One famous example is "Lillibullero," an almost incredibly scurrilous anti-Catholic ballad that swept

England in 1688 when the Protestant William of Orange succeeded his Catholic father-in-law King James II. Macaulay describes this in his *History of England:*

> Public feeling did not then manifest itself by those signs with which we are familiar, by large meetings, and by vehement harangues. Nevertheless it found a vent. Thomas Wharton . . . had written a satirical ballad on the administration of Tyrconnel. In this little poem an Irishman congratulates a brother Irishman, in a barbarous jargon, on the appropriate triumph of Popery and of the Milesian race. The Protestant heir will be excluded. The Protestant officers will be broken. The Great Charter and the praters who appealed to it will be hanged in one rope. The good Talbot will shower commissions on his countrymen, and will cut the throats of the English. . . . The verses and the tune caught the fancy of the nation. From one end of England to the other all classes were constantly singing this idle rhyme. It was especially the delight of the English army.
>
> . . . Wharton afterwards boasted that he had sung a King out of three kingdoms. But in truth the success of Lillibullero was the effect, and not the cause, of that excited state of public feeling which produced the Revolution.

Of the hundreds of political ballads, most are forgotten. They were as ephemeral as the cheap paper on which they were printed—deservedly. But "The Wearin' o' the Green" and "Yankee Doodle" have survived. The Great Depression had its ballad too, and like the English in 1688, the Americans of the 1930's were caught up in the haunting "Brother, Can You Spare a Dime?"

There are parody ballads too. W. S. Gilbert's "Wandering Minstrel" pokes fun at the sentimental and counterfeit drawing-room ballads so popular in the late nineteenth century. For balladry did indeed suffer a decline when prettied up and cleaned up, and when euphemism prevailed. The old comic ballads are apt to be bawdy, and at times they sat ill in an age which referred to legs as limbs. In our century, though, we have our own genteelisms, so it doesn't behoove us to laugh too much at the Victorians.

Another kind of ballad is the love song. Often a moving lament for a lost love, now and then it is a joyous song of ringtime and spring time, overflowing with the glories of love. Sometimes these love songs tell a story, but often the story is vague, or is implied rather than told.

War and work, work and war—these are the themes of many ballads. Miners, lumberjacks, soldiers and sailors, outlaws, mythical heroes like Paul Bunyan and John Henry, mingle with General Washington and President Lincoln in American balladry, and the American Revolution and the Napoleonic Wars appear in hundreds of British songs.

I have placed the ballads in this book in six categories. None is rigid, for many ballads wander over the lines. First, the ballads of magic and miracles. Then the narrative ballads. Third, the political and satiric ballads. Fourth, ballads of soldiers and sailors. Fifth, the work ballads. And last, the songs of the many kinds of love.

"I never heard the old song of Percy and Douglas, that I found not my heart moved more than with a trumpet," said Sir Philip Sidney. Old ballads and new have this power still and will always have it. Here are some chosen from infinite riches.

CONTENTS

I dreamt a dream

&3 MAGIC
& MIRACLES

LADY WEEPING AT THE CROSSROADS

Lady, weeping at the crossroads,
Would you meet your love
In the twilight with his greyhounds,
And the hawk on his glove?

Bribe the birds then on the branches,
Bribe them to be dumb,
Stare the hot sun out of heaven
That the night may come.

Starless are the nights of travel,
Bleak the winter wind;
Run with terror all before you
And regret behind.

Run until you hear the ocean's
Everlasting cry;
Deep though it may be and bitter
You must drink it dry,

Wear out patience in the lowest
Dungeons of the sea,
Searching through the stranded shipwrecks
For the golden key,

Push on to the world's end, pay the
Dread guard with a kiss,
Cross the rotten bridge that totters
Over the abyss.

There stands the deserted castle
Ready to explore;
Enter, climb the marble staircase
Open the locked door.

ঌ 3

Cross the silent empty ballroom,
Doubt and danger past;
Blow the cobwebs from the mirror
See yourself at last.

Put your hand behind the wainscot,
You have done your part;
Find the penknife there and plunge it
Into your false heart.

W. H. AUDEN

THE TRYST

"O whither are you faring to, my sweetheart?
How far now are you journeying, my dear?"
"I am climbing to the brink of yonder hill-top,
Naught human far or near."

"And what will you be seeking there, my sweetheart?
What happy scene is thence surveyed, my dear?"
" 'Twill be night-tide when outwearied I come thither,
And star-shine icy-clear."

"But what will you be brooding on, my sweetheart?
What fantasies of darkness will appear?"
"My self will keep a tryst there—bleak and lonely—
My own heart's secrets I shall share."

"But what will be the manner of your greeting?
What word will you then whisper—no one near?"
"Ah, he who loved me once would know the answer,
Were he still true, my dear."

WALTER DE LA MARE

LOWLANDS

I dreamt a dream the other night.
  Low-laands! Hoo-ray, my John!
I dreamt a dream the other night.
  My Low-lands, a-ray!

I dreamt I saw my own true love.
  Low-laands! Hoo-ray, my John!
I dreamt I saw my own true love.
  My Low-lands, a-ray!

His hair was wet his eyes a-bove.
  Low-laands! Hoo-ray, my John!
His hair was wet his eyes a-bove.
  My Low-lands, a-ray!

All dank his hair and dim his eye.
  Low-laands! Hoo-ray, my John!
All dank his hair and dim his eye.
  My Low-lands, a-ray!

I knew that he had said Good-bye.
  Low-laands! Hoo-ray, my John!
I knew that he had said Good-bye.
  My Low-lands, a-ray!

I bound the wee-per round my head.
  Low-laands! Hoo-ray, my John!
I bound the wee-per round my head.
  My Low-lands, a-ray!

For then I knew my love was dead.
  Low-laands! Hoo-ray, my John!
For then I knew my love was dead.
  My Low-lands, a-ray!

I wish I had ten thousand pound.
Low-laands! Hoo-ray, my John!
I'd steer my ship for miles a-round.
My Low-lands, a-ray!

I'd load her up with grub an' gin.
Low-laands! Hoo-ray, my John!
An' stay in port where I was in.
My Low-lands, a-ray!

I'd stand ye drink three times a day.
Low-laands! Hoo-ray, my John!
An' feed ye well an' raise yer pay.
My Low-lands, a-ray!

THE OLD KING

Woke—the old King of Cumberland:
   Yet breathed not nor stirred,
But crouched in the darkness, hearkening after
   A voice he had heard.

He leaned upon his foursquare bed,
   Thumb beneath bristling chin;
"Alas, alas!—the woeful dream—
   The dream that I was in!"

The old, old King of Cumberland
   Muttered, " 'Twas not the sea
Gushing upon Schlievlisskin rocks
   That wakened me.

"Thunder from midmost night it was not,
   For yonder at those bars
Burn fiercely toward the Eastern deeps
   The summer stars."

The old, old King of Cumberland
   Mused yet, "Rats ever did
Ramp, rustle, clink my spurs, and gnaw
   My coverlid.

"Oft hath a furtive midnight breeze
   Along this valance skirred;
But in this stagnant calm 'twas not
   The wind I heard.

"Some keener, stranger, quieter, closer
   Voice it was me woke . . ."
And silence, like a billow, drowned
   The word he spoke.

Fixed now his stare, for limned in dark,
    Gazing from cowl-like hood,
Stark in the vague, all-listening night,
    A shadow stood.

Sudden a gigantic hand he thrust
    Into his bosom cold,
Where now no surging restless beat
    Its long tale told.

Swept on him then, as there he sate,
    Terror icy chill:
'Twas silence that had him awoke—
    His heart stood still.

WALTER DE LA MARE

BALLAD

I dreamed I passed a doorway
Where, for a sign of death,
White ribbons one was binding
About a flowery wreath.

What drew me so, I know not,
But drawing near, I said,
"Kind sir, and can you tell me
Who is it here lies dead?"

Said he, "Your most belovèd
Dead here this very day,
That had known twenty Aprils,
Had she but lived till May."

Astonished, I made answer,
"Good sir, how say you so!
Here have I no belovèd,
This house I do not know."

Said he, "Who from forever
Was destined so to be
Here lies, your true belovèd,
Whom you shall never see."

I dreamed I passed a doorway
Where, for a sign of death,
White ribbons one was binding
About a flowery wreath.

JOHN HALL WHEELOCK

THE QUEEN OF ELFAN'S NOURICE

I heard a cow low, a bonnie cow low,
    An a cow low down in yon glen;
Lang, lang will my young son greet
    Or his mither bid him come ben.

I heard a cow low, a bonnie cow low,
    An a cow low down in yon fauld;
Lang, lang will my young son greet [1]
    Or his mither take him frae cauld.

.   .   .   .   .

   .   .   .   .   .

Waken, Queen of Elfan,
    An hear your nourice moan.

"O moan ye for your meat,
    Or moan ye for your fee,
Or moan ye for the ither bounties
    That ladies are wont to gie?"

"I moan na for my meat,
    Nor moan I for my fee,
Nor moan I for the ither bounties
    That ladies are wont to gie.

.   .   .   .   .

   .   .   .   .   .

But I moan for my young son
    I left in four nights auld.

[1] weep

꒜ *11*

"I moan na for my meat,
   Nor yet for my fee,
But I moan for Christen land,
   It's there I fain would be."

"O nurse my bairn, nourice," she says,
   "Till he stan at your knee,
An ye's win hame to Christen land,
   Whar fain it 's ye wad be.

"O keep my bairn, nourice,
   Till he gang by the hauld,
An ye 's win hame to your young son
   Ye left in four nights auld."

"O nourice lay your head
   Upo my knee:
See ye na that narrow road
   Up by yon tree?

.   .   .   .   .

  .   .   .   .

That's the road the righteous goes,
   And that's the road to heaven.

"An see na ye that braid road,
   Down by yon sunny fell?
Yon 's the road the wicked gae,
   An that's the road to hell."

TAM LIN

O I forbid you, maidens a',
   That wear gowd on your hair,
To come or gae by Carterhaugh,
   For young Tam Lin is there.

There's nane that gaes by Carterhaugh
   But they leave him a wad,
Either their rings, or green mantles,
   Or else their maidenhead.

Janet has kilted her green kirtle
   A little aboon her knee,
And she has broded her yellow hair
   A little aboon her bree.[1]
And she's awa to Carterhaugh,
   As fast as she can hie.

When she came to Carterhaugh
   Tam Lin was at the well,
And there she fand his steed standing,
   But away was himsel.

She had na pu'd a double rose,
   A rose but only twa,
Till up then started young Tam Lin,
   Says, Lady, thou 's pu nae mae.

Why pu's thou the rose, Janet,
   And why breaks thou the wand?
Or why comes thou to Carterhaugh
   Withoutten my command?

[1] above her brow

ᔐ 13

"Carterhaugh, it is my ain,
   My daddy gave it me;
I'll come and gang by Carterhaugh,
   And ask nae leave at thee."

Janet has kilted her green kirtle
   A little aboon her knee,
And she has snooded her yellow hair
   A little aboon her bree,
And she is to her father's ha,
   As fast as she can hie.

Four and twenty ladies fair
   Were playing at the ba,
And out then cam the fair Janet,
   Ance the flower amang them a'.

Four and twenty ladies fair
   Were playing at the chess,
And out then cam the fair Janet,
   As green as onie glass.

Out then spak an auld grey knight,
   Lay oer the castle wa,
And says, Alas, fair Janet, for thee
   But we'll be blamed a'.

"Haud your tongue, ye auld fac'd knight,
   Some ill death may ye die!
Father my bairn on whom I will,
   I'll father nane on thee."

Out then spak her father dear,
   And he spak meek and mild;
"And ever alas, sweet Janet," he says,
   "I think thou gaes wi child."

"If that I gae wi child, father,
    Mysel maun bear the blame;
There's neer a laird about your ha
    Shall get the bairn's name.

"If my love were an earthly knight,
    As he 's an elfin grey,
I wad na gie my ain true-love
    For nae lord that ye hae.

"The steed that my true-love rides on
    Is lighter than the wind;
Wi siller he is shod before,
    Wi burning gowd behind."

Janet has kilted her green kirtle
    A little aboon her knee,
And she has snooded her yellow hair
    A little aboon her bree,
And she's awa to Carterhaugh,
    As fast as she can hie.

When she cam to Carterhaugh,
    Tam Lin was at the well,
And there she fand his steed standing,
    But away was himsel.

She had na pu'd a double rose,
    A rose but only twa,
Till up then started young Tam Lin,
    Says, Lady, thou pu's nae mae.

Why pu's thou the rose, Janet,
    Among the groves sae green,
And a' to kill the bonie babe
    That we gat us between?

"O tell me, tell me, Tam Lin," she says,
    "For 's sake that died on tree,
If eer ye was in holy chapel,
    Or christendom did see?"

"Roxbrugh he was my grandfather,
    Took me with him to bide,
And ance it fell upon a day
    That wae [2] did me betide.

"And ance it fell upon a day,
    A cauld day and a snell,[3]
When we were frae the hunting come
    That frae my horse I fell;
The Queen o Fairies she caught me,
    In yon green hill to dwell.

"And pleasant is the fairy land,
    But, an eerie tale to tell,
Ay at the end of seven years
    We pay a tiend [4] to hell;
I am sae fair and fu o flesh,
    I'm feard it be mysel.

"But the night is Halloween, lady,
    The morn is Hallowday;
Then win me, win me, an ye will,
    For weel I wat ye may.

"Just at the mirk and midnight hour
    The fairy folk will ride,
And they that wad their true-love win,
    At Miles Cross they maun bide."

[2] woe   [3] chilly   [4] tithe

16

"But how shall I thee ken, Tam Lin,
    Or how my true-love know,
Amang sae mony unco knights
    The like I never saw?"

"O first let pass the black, lady,
    And syne let pass the brown,
But quickly run to the milk-white steed,
    Pu ye his rider down.

"For I'll ride on the milk-white steed
    And ay nearest the town:
Because I was an earthly knight
    They gie me that renown.

"My right hand will be glovd, lady,
    My left hand will be bare,
Cockt up shall my bonnet be,
    And kaimd down shall my hair,
And thae 's the takens I gie thee,
    Nae doubt I will be there.

"They'll turn me in your arms, lady,
    Into an esk [5] and adder;
But hold me fast, and fear me not,
    I am your bairn's father.

"They'll turn me to a bear sae grim,
    And then a lion bold;
But hold me fast, and fear me not,
    As ye shall love your child.

[5] newt

ॐ *17*

"Again they'll turn me in your arms
    To a red het gaud of airn [6];
But hold me fast, and fear me not
    I'll do to you nae harm.

"And last they'll turn me in your arms
    Into the burning gleed [7];
Then throw me into well water,
    O throw me in wi speed.

"And then I'll be your ain true-love,
    I'll turn a naked knight;
Then cover me wi your green mantle,
    And cover me out o sight."

Gloomy, gloomy was the night,
    And eerie was the way,
As fair Jenny in her green mantle
    To Miles Cross she did gae.

About the middle o the night
    She heard the bridles ring;
This lady was as glad at that
    As any earthly thing.

First she let the black pass by,
    And syne she let the brown;
But quickly she ran to the milk-white steed,
    And pu'd the rider down.

Sae weel she minded what he did say,
    And young Tam Lin did win:
Syne covered him wi her green mantle,
    As blythe 's a bird in spring.

[6] iron   [7] ember

ॐ *18*

Out then spak the Queen o Fairies,
    Out of a bush o broom:
"Them that has gotten young Tam Lin
    Has gotten a stately groom."

Out then spak the Queen o Fairies,
    And an angry woman was she:
"Shame betide her ill-far'd face,
    And an ill death may she die,
For she 's taen awa the boniest knight
    In a' my companie.

"But had I kend, Tam Lin," she says,
    "What now this night I see,
I wad hae taen out thy twa grey een,
    And put in twa een o tree.[8]"

[8] wood

TAM LIN

She's taen her petticoat by the band,
   Her mantle owre her arm,
And she's awa to Chester wood,
   As fast as she could run.

She scarsely pulled a rose, a rose,
   She scarse pulled two or three,
Till up there starts Thomas
   On the Lady Margaret's knee.

She's taen her petticoat by the band,
   Her mantle owre her arm,
And Lady Margaret's gane hame agen,
   As fast as she could run.

Up starts Lady Margaret's sister,
   An angry woman was she:
"If there ever was a woman wi child,
   Margaret, you are wi!"

Up starts Lady Margaret's mother,
   An angry woman was she:
"There grows ane herb in yon kirk-yard
   That will scathe the babe away."

She took her petticoats by the band,
   Her mantle owre her arm,
And she's gane to yon kirk-yard
   As fast as she could run.

A variant "Tam Lin"

She scarsely pulled an herb, an herb,
    She scarse pulled two or three,
Till up starts there Thomas
    Upon this Lady Margret's knee.

"How dare ye pull a rose?" he says,
    "How dare ye break the tree?
How dare ye pull this herb," he says,
    "To scathe my babe away?

"This night is Halloweve," he said,
    "Our court is going to waste,
And them that loves their true-love best
    At Chester bridge they'll meet.

"First let pass the black," he says,
    "And then let pass the brown,
But when ye meet the milk-white steed,
    Pull ye the rider down.

"They'll turn me to an eagle," he says,
    "And then into an ass;
Come, hold me fast, and fear me not,
    The man that you love best.

"They'll turn me to a flash of fire,
    And then to a naked man;
Come, wrap you your mantle me about,
    And then you'll have me won."

She took her petticoats by the band,
    Her mantle owre her arm,
And she's awa to Chester bridge,
    As fast as she could run.

And first she did let pass the black,
    And then let pass the brown,
But when she met the milk-white steed,
    She pulled the rider down.

They turned him in her arms an eagle,
    And then into an ass;
But she held him fast, and feared him not,
    The man that she loved best.

They turned him into a flash of fire,
    And then into a naked man;
But she wrapped her mantle him about,
    And then she had him won.

"O wae be to ye, Lady Margaret,
    And an ill death may you die,
For you've robbed me of the bravest knight
    That eer rode in our company."

THOMAS RYMER

True Thomas lay o'er yond grassy bank,
  And he beheld a ladie gay,
A ladie that was brisk and bold,
  Come riding oer the fernie brae.

Her skirt was of the grass-green silk,
  Her mantel of the velvet fine,
At ilka tett of her horse's mane
  Hung fifty silver bells and nine.

True Thomas he took off his hat,
  And bowed him low down till his knee:
"All hail, thou mighty Queen of Heaven,
  For your peer on earth I never did see."

"O no, O no, true Thomas," she says,
  "That name does not belong to me,
I am but the queen of fair Elfland,
  And I'm come here for to visit thee.

"But ye maun go wi me now, Thomas,
  True Thomas, ye maun go wi me,
For ye maun serve me seven years,
  Thro well or wae as may chance to be."

She turned about her milk-white steed,
  And took true Thomas up behind,
And aye wheneer her bridle rang,
  The steed flew swifter than the wind.

For forty days and forty nights
  He wade thro red blude to the knee,
And he saw neither sun nor moon,
  But heard the roaring of the sea.

O they rade on, and further on,
    Until they came to a garden green:
"Light down, light down, ye ladie free,
    Some of that fruit let me pull to thee."

"O no, O no, True Thomas," she says,
    "That fruit maun not be touched by thee,
For a' the plagues that are in hell
    Light on the fruit of this countrie.

"But I have a loaf here in my lap,
    Likewise a bottle of claret wine,
And now ere we go farther on,
    We'll rest a while, and ye may dine."

When he had eaten and drunk his fill,
    "Lay down your head upon my knee,"
The lady sayd, "ere we climb yon hill,
    And I will show you fairlies [1] three.

"O see not ye yon narrow road,
    So thick beset wi thorns and briers?
That is the path of righteousness,
    Tho after it but few enquires.

"And see not ye that braid braid road,
    That lies across yon lillie leven?
That is the path of wickedness,
    Tho some call it the road to heaven.

"And see not ye that bonny road,
    Which winds about the fernie brae?
That is the road to fair Elfland,
    Where you and I this night maun gae.

[1] wonders

&❧ 24

"But Thomas, ye maun hold your tongue,
  Whatever you may hear or see,
For gin ae word you should chance to speak,
  You will ne'er get back to your ain countrie."

He has gotten a coat of the elven cloth,
  And a pair of shoes of velvet green,
And till seven years were past and gone
  True Thomas on earth was never seen.

PROUD MAISIE

Proud Maisie is in the wood
   Walking so early;
Sweet Robin sits on the bush,
  Singing so rarely.

"Tell me, thou bonny bird,
   When shall I marry me?"
"When six braw gentlemen
  Kirkward shall carry ye."

"Who makes the bridal bed,
   Birdie, say truly?"
"The grey-headed sexton
   That delves the grave duly.

"The glow-worm o'er grave and stone
   Shall light thee steady;
The owl from the steeple sing
  'Welcome, proud lady!' "

SIR WALTER SCOTT

THE CRYSTAL CABINET

The maiden caught me in the wild,
  Where I was dancing merrily;
She put me into her cabinet,
  And locked me up with a golden key.

This cabinet is formed of gold,
  And pearl and crystal shining bright,
And within it opens into a world
  And a little lovely moony night.

Another England there I saw,
  Another London with its Tower,
Another Thames and other hills,
  And another pleasant Surrey bower.

Another maiden like herself,
  Translucent, lovely, shining clear,
Threefold, each in the other closed—
  O, what a pleasant trembling fear!

O, what a smile! A threefold smile
  Filled me that like a flame I burned;
I bent to kiss the lovely maid,
  And found a threefold kiss returned.

I strove to seize the inmost form
  With ardour fierce and hands of flame,
But burst the crystal cabinet,
  And like a weeping babe became:

A weeping babe upon the wild,
  And weeping woman pale reclined,
And in the outward air again,
  I filled with woes the passing wind.

WILLIAM BLAKE

LA BELLE DAME SANS MERCI

(Original Version)

O what can ail thee, knight-at-arms,
    Alone and palely loitering?
The sedge has wither'd from the lake,
    And no birds sing.

O what can ail thee, knight-at-arms,
    So haggard, and so woe-begone?
The squirrel's granary is full,
    And the harvest's done.

I se a lily on thy brow,
    With anguish moist and fever dew,
And on thy cheeks a fading rose
    Fast withereth too.

I met a lady in the meads,
    Full beautiful—a faery's child,
Her hair was long, her foot was light,
    And her eyes were wild.

I made a garland for her head,
    And bracelets too, and fragrant zone;
She look'd at me as she did love,
    And made sweet moan.

I set her on my pacing steed,
    And nothing else saw all day long,
For sidelong would she bend and sing
    A faery's song.

She found me roots of relish sweet,
    And honey wild, and manna dew,
And sure in language strange she said
    "I love thee true."

She took me to her elfin grot,
    And there she wept and sigh'd full sore,
And there I shut her wild wild eyes
    With kisses four.

And there she lulled me asleep,
    And there I dream'd—Ah! woe betide!
The latest dream I ever dream'd
    On the cold hill's side.

I saw pale kings and princes too,
    Pale warriors, death-pale were they all;
They cried, "La Belle Dame sans Merci
    Hath thee in thrall!"

I saw their starved lips in the gloam,
    With horrid warning gaped wide,
And I awoke, and found me here,
    On the cold hill's side.

And this is why I sojourn here,
    Alone and palely loitering,
Though the sedge is wither'd from the lake,
    And no birds sing.

JOHN KEATS

TOM'S ANGEL

No one was in the fields
But me and Polly Flint,
When, like a giant across the grass,
The flaming angel went.

It was budding time in May,
And green as green could be,
And all in his height he went along
Past Polly Flint and me.

We'd been playing in the woods,
And Polly up, and ran,
And hid her face, and said,
"Tom! Tom! The Man! The Man!"

And I up-turned; and there,
Like flames across the sky,
With wings all bristling, came
The Angel striding by.

And a chaffinch overhead
Kept whistling in the tree
While the Angel, blue as fire, came on
Past Polly Flint and me.

And I saw his hair, and all
The ruffling of his hem,
As over the clovers his bare feet
Trod without stirring them.

Polly—she cried; and, oh!
We ran, until the lane
Turned by the miller's roaring wheel,
And we were safe again.

WALTER DE LA MARE

FATHER GILLIGAN

The old priest Peter Gilligan
   Was weary night and day,
For half his flock were in their beds,
   Or under green sods lay.

Once while he nodded on a chair,
   At the moth-hour of eve,
Another poor man sent for him,
   And he began to grieve.

"I have no rest, nor joy, nor peace,
   For people die and die;"
And after cried he, "God forgive!
   My body spake, not I!"

And then, half-lying on the chair,
   He knelt, prayed, fell asleep;
And the moth-hour went from the fields,
   And stars began to peep.

They slowly into millions grew,
   And leaves shook in the wind;
And God covered the world with shade,
   And whispered to mankind.

Upon the time of sparrow chirp
   When the moths came once more,
The old priest Peter Gilligan
   Stood upright on the floor.

"*Mavrone, mavrone!* the man has died,
   While I slept on the chair;"
He roused his horse out of its sleep,
   And rode with little care.

He rode now as he never rode,
   By rocky lane and fen;
The sick man's wife opened the door:
   "Father! you come again!"

"And is the poor man dead?" he cried.
   "He died an hour ago."
The old priest Peter Gilligan
   In grief swayed to and fro.

"When you were gone he turned and died,
   As merry as a bird."
The old priest Peter Gilligan
   He knelt him at that word.

"He who hath made the night of stars
   For souls who tire and bleed,
Sent one of His great angels down
   To help me in my need.

"He who is wrapped in purple robes,
   With planets in his care,
Had pity on the least of things
   Asleep upon a chair."

W. B. YEATS

THE BALLAD OF BEFANA

An Epiphany Legend

Befana the Housewife, scrubbing her pane,
Saw three old sages ride down the lane,
Saw three gray travelers pass her door—
Gaspar, Balthazar, Melchior.

"Where journey you, sirs?" she asked of them.
Balthazar answered, "To Bethlehem,

For we have news of a marvelous thing.
Born in a stable is Christ the King."

"Give Him my welcome!"
Then Gaspar smiled,
"Come with us, mistress, to greet the Child."

"Oh, happily, happily would I fare,
Were my dusting through and I'd polished the stair."

Old Melchior leaned on his saddle horn.
"Then send but a gift to the small Newborn."

"Oh, gladly, gladly I'd send Him one,
Were the hearthstone swept and my weaving done.

"As soon as ever I've baked my bread,
I'll fetch Him a pillow for His head,
And a coverlet too," Befana said.

"When the rooms are aired and the linen dry,
I'll look at the Babe."
But the Three rode by.

She worked for a day and a night and a day,
Then, gifts in her hands, took up her way.
But she never could find where the Christ Child lay.

And still she wanders at Christmastide,
Houseless, whose house was all her pride,

Whose heart was tardy, whose gifts were late;
Wanders, and knocks at every gate,
Crying, "Good people, the bells begin!
Put off your toiling and let love in."

PHYLLIS MCGINLEY

THE FARMER'S CURST WIFE

There was an old farmer in Sussex did dwell,
        (*Chorus of whistlers*)
There was an old farmer in Sussex did dwell,
And he had a bad wife, as many knew well.
        (*Chorus of whistlers*)

Then Satan came to the old man at the plough:
"One of your family I must have now.

"It is not your eldest son that I crave,
But it is your old wife, and she I will have."

"O welcome, good Satan, with all my heart!
I hope you and she will never more part."

Now Satan has got the old wife on his back,
And he lugged her along, like a pedlar's pack.

He trudged away till they came to his hall-gate;
Says he, "Here, take in an old Sussex chap's mate."

O then she did kick the young imps about;
Says one to the other, "Let's try turn her out."

She spied thirteen imps all dancing in chains,
She up with her pattens and beat out their brains.

She knocked the old Satan against the wall:
"Let's turn her out, or she'll murder us all."

Now he's bundled her up on his back amain,
And to her old husband he took her again.

"I have been a tormentor the whole of my life,
But I ne'er was tormented so as with your wife."

ই৯ 35

THE CURST WIFE

The old Devil he came to a woodsman one day.
Said he, "One of your family I would take away."
    Ti-rum-ti-diddle-dum-dido.

"Oh," said the woodsman, "I'm all undone.
For I hate to lose my oldest son."
    Ti-rum-ti-diddle-dum-dido.

"It's not your oldest son I crave,
But your scolding wife I'm bound to have."
    Ti-rum-ti-diddle-dum-dido.

"Oh, take her and welcome with all my heart.
I hope you two never more will part."
    Ti-rum-ti-diddle-dum-dido.

The Devil he took her upon his back
And off to Hell went clickty-clack.
    Ti-rum-ti-diddle-dum-dido.

One little devil cried out in his pains;
She picked up a club and knocked out his brains.
    Ti-rum-ti-diddle-dum-dido.

Another little devil climbed up on the wall,
Saying, "Take her back, Daddy, she'll murder us all."
    Ti-rum-ti-diddle-dum-dido.

Another little devil jumped into the well,
Saying, "Take her away, Dad, she'll ruin all Hell."
    Ti-rum-ti-diddle-dum-dido.

American version

⇛ 36

So the Devil he roped her up in a sack
And off to the woodsman he carried her back.
    Ti-rum-ti-diddle-dum-dido.

The woodsman he laughed, for it tickled him well
For to think that his wife was the bully of Hell.
    Ti-rum-ti-diddle-dum-dido.

THE WEE WEE MAN

As I was wa'king all alone,
　　Between a water and a wa,
And there I spy'd a wee wee man,
　　And he was the least that ere I saw.

His legs were scarce a shathmount's [1] length,
　　And thick and thimber was his thigh;
Between his brows there was a span,
　　And between his shoulders there was three.

He took up a meikle stane,
　　And he flang 't as far as I could see;
Though I had been a Wallace wight,
　　I couldna liften 't to my knee.

"O wee wee man, but thou be strang!
　　O tell me where thy dwelling be?"
"My dwelling's down at yon bonny bower;
　　O will you go with me and see?"

On we lap, and awa we rade,
　　Till we came to yon bonny green;
We lighted down for to bait our horse,
　　And out there came a lady fine.

Four and twenty at her back,
　　And they were a' clad out in green;
Though the King of Scotland had been there,
　　The warst o them might hae been his queen.

[1] a handspan—about 6 inches

On we lap, and awa we rade,
   Till we came to yon bonny ha,
Whare the roof was o the beaten gould,
   And the floor was o the cristal a'.

When we came to the stair-foot,
   Ladies were dancing, jimp and sma,
But in the twinkling of an eye,
   My wee wee man was clean awa.

THE DEMON LOVER

"O where have you been, my dear, dear love,
   This long seven years and more?"
"O I'm come to seek my former vows
   Ye granted me before."

"O hold your tongue of your former vows,
   For they will breed sad strife;
O hold your tongue of your former vows,
   For I am become a wife."

He turned him right and round about,
   And the tear blinded his ee;
"I would never have trodden on Irish ground,
   If it had not been for thee.

"I might have had a king's daughtér,
   Far, far beyond the sea;
I might have had a king's daughtér,
   Were it not for love of thee."

"If ye might have had a king's daughtér,
   Yourself ye had to blame;
Ye might have taken the king's daughtér,
   For ye kenned that I was nane.[1]

"If I were to leave my husband dear,
   And my two babes also,
O what have you to take me to,
   If with you I should go?"

[1] none

"I have seven ships upon the sea,
    The eighth brought me to land;
With four and twenty bold mariners.
    And music on every hand."

She has taken up her two little babes,
    Kissed them both cheek and chin;
"O fare ye well, my own two babes,
    For I'll never see you again."

She set her foot upon the ship,
    No mariners could she behold;
But the sails were of the taffety,
    And the masts of the beaten gold.

She had not sailed a league, a league,
    A league but barely three,
When dismal grew his countenance,
    And drumlie ² grew his ee.

They had not sailed a league, a league,
    A league but barely three,
Until she espied his cloven foot,
    And she wept right bitterly.

"O hold your tongue of your weeping," says he,
    "Of your weeping now let me be;
I will show you how the lilies grow
    On the banks of Italy."

"O what hills are they, those pleasant hills,
    That the sun shines sweetly on?"
"O those are the hills of Heaven," he said,
    "Where you shall never wone.³ "

---

² gloomy   ³ live

"O whaten [4] a mountain is that," she said,
  "So dreary with frost and snow?"
"O that is the mountain of Hell," he cried,
  "Where you and I must go."

He struck the top-mast with his hand,
  The fore-mast with his knee;
And he brake that gallant ship in twain,
  And sank her in the sea.

[4] what kind of

&> 42

THE WIFE OF USHER'S WELL

There lived a wife at Usher's well,
    And a wealthy wife was she;
She had three stout and stalwart sons,
    And sent them o'er the sea.

They hadna been a week from her,
    A week but barely ane,
When word came to the carline wife [1]
    That her three sons were gane.

They hadna been a week from her,
    A week but barely three,
When word came to the carline wife
    That her sons she'd never see.

"I wish the wind may never cease,
    Nor fashes [2] in the flood,
Till my three sons come hame to me
    In earthly flesh and blood!"

It fell about the Martinmas,
    When nights are lang and mirk,
The carline wife's three sons came hame,
    And their hats were o' the birk.

It neither grew in syke [3] nor ditch,
    Nor yet in ony sheugh; [4]
But at the gates o' Paradise
    That birk grew fair eneugh.

---

[1] old woman   [2] trouble   [3] marsh   [4] trench

"Blow up the fire, my maidens!
    Bring water from the well!
For a' my house shall feast this night,
    Since my three sons are well."

And she has made to them a bed,
    She's made it large and wide;
And she 's ta'en her mantle her about,
    Sat down at the bedside.

Up then crew the red, red cock,
    And up and crew the gray;
The eldest to the youngest said,
    " 'Tis time we were away."

The cock he hadna craw'd but once,
    And clapp'd his wings at a',
When the youngest to the eldest said,
    "Brother, we must awa'.

"The cock doth craw, the day doth daw,
    The channerin' worm doth chide;
Gin we be miss'd out o' our place,
    A sair pain we maun bide."—

"Lie still, lie still but a little wee while,
    Lie still but if we may;
Gin my mother should miss us when she wakes,
    She'll go mad ere it be day."—

"Fare ye weel, my mother dear!
    Fareweel to barn and byre!
And fare ye weel, the bonny lass
    That kindles my mother's fire!"

THE WIFE OF USHER'S WELL

There lived a lady, a lady gay,
O children she had three,
She sent them away to the northern school
To learn their grammars three.

They hadn't been gone but a very short time,
Scarcely three weeks and a day,
Till death, sweet death come hastening along
And stole those babes away.

There is a king in heaven, cried she,
A king of the third degree.
Send back, send back my three little babes,
This night send them back to me.

She made them a bed in the backward room,
And on it put a neat white sheet,
And over the top a golden spread,
Much better that they might sleep.

Take it off, take it off, cried the oldest one,
Take it off, take it off, cried he,
For what's to become of this wide wicked world
Since sin has first begun.

She spread them a table of bread and wine,
As neat as neat could be,
Come eat, come drink, my three little babes,
Come eat, come drink with me.

This American version of a famous British ballad is infinitely touching
in its mingling of grief and resignation to God's will.

ॐ 45

I cannot eat your bread, says one,
Neither can I drink your wine,
For my Saviour dear is standing near,
To him we must resign.

Cold clay, cold clay hangs over my head,
Green grass grows over my feet;
And every tear that you shed for me
Doth wet my winding sheet.

THE KING'S SON

Who rideth through the driving rain
   At such a headlong speed?
Naked and pale he rides amain
   Upon a naked steed.

Nor hollow nor height his going bars,
   His wet steed shines like silk,
His head is golden to the stars
   And his limbs are white as milk.

But, lo, he dwindles as the light
   That lifts from a black mere,
And, as the fair youth wanes from sight,
   The steed grows mightier.

What wizard by yon holy tree
   Mutters unto the sky
Where Macha's flame-tongued horses flee
   On hoofs of thunder by?

Ah, 'tis not holy so to ban
   The youth of kingly seed:
Ah! woe, the wasting of a man
   Who changes to a steed!

Nightly upon the Plain of Kings,
   When Macha's day is nigh,
He gallops; and the dark wind brings
   His lonely human cry.

THOMAS BOYD

PARDONER'S TALE BLUES

I am Death, all bone and hair
   Mother, let me in
Get no health from this country air
   Mother, let me in.

What shall I do till Death can die?
What shall I do till he lies down
Till he lies down with his eyes at rest?
What shall I do till he dies?

Yes, God made me to live forever
   Mother, let me in
No deep earth and no deep river
   Mother, let me in.

Well run along men, to your bag of gold
   Mother, let me in
I cannot laugh, I am too old
   Mother, let me in.

And I knock upon the ground with my staff
   Mother, let me in
I can joke though I cannot laugh
   Mother, let me in.

PATRICIA BEER

THE UNQUIET GRAVE

So cold the wintry winds do blow
And down fell drops of rain.
I have had but one true love,
In greenwood she was slain.

I'll say as much for my true love
As any young man could say.
I'll sit and I'll weep on her cold grave
For a twelve month and a day.

When the twelve month and a day was up
The ghost began to weep.
Why do you sit here on my grave
And will not let me sleep?

There's one thing more that I do want
And that is all I crave,
And that is to kiss your lily-white lips
And I will go from your grave.

My lips they are as cold as clay,
My breath smells heavy and strong,
And if you kiss my lily-white lips
Your time will not be long.

Down in the garden of myrtle green
Where my true love and me did walk
The finest flower that ever was seen
Is withered unto the stalk.

The stalk is withered unto the root
And the root unto the ground.
That's why I mourn for the loss of my love
When she's not here to be found.

SWEET WILLIAM'S GHOST

There came a ghost to Margret's door,
   With many a grievous groan,
And ay he tirled at the pin,
   But answer made she none.

"Is that my father Philip,
   Or is 't my brother John?
Or is 't my true-love, Willy,
   From Scotland new come home?"

" 'T is not thy father Philip,
   Nor yet thy brother John;
But 't is thy true-love, Willy,
   From Scotland new come home.

"O sweet Margret, O dear Margret,
   I pray thee speak to me;
Give me my faith and troth, Margret,
   As I gave it to thee."

"Thy faith and troth thou 's never get,
   Nor yet will I thee lend,
Till that thou come within my bower,
   And kiss my cheek and chin."

"If I shoud come within thy bower,
   I am no earthly man;
And shoud I kiss thy rosy lips,
   Thy days will not be lang.

"O sweet Margret, O dear Margret,
   I pray thee speak to me;
Give me my faith and troth, Margret,
   As I gave it to thee."

"Thy faith and troth thou 's never get,
   Nor yet will I thee lend,
Till you take me to yon kirk,
   And wed me with a ring."

"My bones are buried in yon kirk-yard,
   Afar beyond the sea,
And it is but my spirit, Margret,
   That 's now speaking to thee."

She stretchd out her lilly-white hand,
   And, for to do her best,
"Hae, there 's your faith and troth, Willy,
   God send your soul good rest."

Now she has kilted her robes of green
   A piece below her knee,
And a' the live-lang winter night
   The dead corp followed she.

"Is there any room at your head, Willy?
   Or any room at your feet?
Or any room at your side, Willy,
   Wherein that I may creep?"

"There 's no room at my head, Margret,
   There 's no room at my feet;
There 's no room at my side, Margret,
   My coffin 's made so meet."

Then up and crew the red, red cock,
   And up then crew the gray:
"Tis time, tis time, my dear Margret,
   That you were going away."

No more the ghost to Margret said,
 But, with a grievous groan,
Evanishd in a cloud of mist,
 And left her all alone.

"O stay, my only true-love, stay,"
 The constant Margret cry'd;
Wan grew her cheeks, she closd her een,
 Stretchd her soft limbs, and dy'd.

EVENING

Prince Absalom and Sir Rotherham Redde
Rode on a rocking-horse home to bed,

With dreams like cherries ripening big
Beneath the frondage of each wig.

In a flat field on the road to Sleep
They ride together, a-hunting sheep

That like the swan-bright fountains seem;
Their tails hang down as meek as a dream.

Prince Absalom seems a long-fleeced bush,
The heat's tabernacle, in the hush

And the glamour of eve, when buds the dew
Into bright tales that never come true;

And as he passes a cherry-tree,
Caught by his long hair, bound is he,

While all his gold fleece flows like water
Into the lap of Sir Rotherham's daughter.

Come, then, and sit upon the grass
With cherries to pelt you as bright as glass—

Vermilion bells that sound as clear
As the bright swans whose sighing you hear

When they float to their crystal death
Of water, scarcely plumed by the breath

Of air—so clear in the round leaves
They look, this crystal sound scarce grieves,

As they pelt down like tears fall'n bright
From music or some deep delight.

The gardener cut off his beard of bast
And tied up the fountain-tree, made it fast

And bound it together till who could see
Which is Prince Absalom, which is the tree?

Only his gold fleece flows like water
Into the lap of Sir Rotherham's daughter;

Sir Rotherham Redde gathers bags of gold
Instead of the cherries ruddy and cold.

EDITH SITWELL

BINNORIE

There were twa sisters sat in a bour;
   Binnorie, O Binnorie!
There cam a knight to be their wooer,
   By the bonnie milldams o' Binnorie.

He courted the eldest with glove and ring,
But he lo'ed the youngest abune a' thing.

The eldest she was vexèd sair,
And sair envìed her sister fair.

Upon a morning fair and clear,
She cried upon her sister dear:

"O sister, sister, tak my hand,
And we'll see our father's ships to land."

She 's ta'en her by the lily hand,
And led her down to the river-strand.

The youngest stood up on a stane,
The eldest cam and push'd her in.

"O sister, sister, reach your hand!
And ye sall be heir o' half my land:

"O sister, reach me but your glove!
And sweet William sall be your love."

"Foul fa' the hand that I should take;
It twin'd [1] me o' my warldis make. [2]

[1] robbed   [2] my one mate in the world

🐦 55

"Your cherry cheeks and your yellow hair
Gar'd me gang maiden evermair."

Sometimes she sank, sometimes she swam,
Until she cam to the miller's dam.

Out then cam the miller's son,
And saw the fair maid soummin'[3] in.

"O father, father, draw your dam!
There's either a mermaid or a milk-white swan."

The miller hasted and drew his dam,
And there he found a drown'd woman.

You couldna see her middle sma',
Her gowden girdle was sae braw.

You couldna see her lily feet,
Her gowden fringes were sae deep.

You couldna see her yellow hair
For the strings o' pearls was twisted there.

You couldna see her fingers sma',
Wi' diamond rings they were cover'd a'.

And by there cam a harper fine,
That harpit to the king at dine.

And when he look'd that lady on,
He sigh'd and made a heavy moan.

[3] swimming

ु⸙ 56

He 's made a harp of her breast-bane,
Whose sound wad melt a heart of stane.

He 's ta'en three locks o' her yellow hair,
And wi' them strung his harp sae rare.

He went into her father's hall,
And there was the court assembled all.

He laid his harp upon a stane,
And straight it began to play by lane.[4]

"O yonder sits my father, the King,
And yonder sits my mother, the Queen;

"And yonder stands my brother Hugh,
And by him my William, sweet and true."

But the last tune that the harp play'd then—
 Binnorie, O Binnorie!
Was, "Woe to my sister, false Helèn!"
 By the bonnie milldams o' Binnorie.

[4] by itself

  57

IS IT FAR TO GO

Is it far to go?
   A step—no further.
Is it hard to go?
   Ask the melting snow,
   The eddying feather.

What can I take there?
   Not a hank, not a hair.
What shall I leave behind?
   Ask the hastening wind,
   The fainting star.

Shall I be gone long?
   For ever and a day.
To whom there belong?
   Ask the stone to say,
   Ask my song.

Who will say farewell?
   The beating bell.
Will anyone miss me?
   That I dare not tell—
   Quick, Rose, and kiss me.

C. DAY LEWIS

So daring in love,
and so dauntless in war

✒ *NARRATIVES*

THE DESTRUCTION OF SENNACHERIB

The Assyrian came down like the wolf on the fold,
And his cohorts were gleaming in purple and gold;
And the sheen of their spears was like stars on the sea,
When the blue wave rolls nightly on deep Galilee.

Like the leaves of the forest when Summer is green,
That host with their banners at sunset were seen:
Like the leaves of the forest when Autumn hath blown,
That host on the morrow lay wither'd and strown.

For the Angel of Death spread his wings on the blast,
And breathed in the face of the foe as he pass'd;
And the eyes of the sleepers wax'd deadly and chill,
And their hearts but once heaved, and for ever grew still!

And there lay the steed with his nostril all wide,
But through it there roll'd not the breath of his pride;
And the foam of his gasping lay white on the turf,
And cold as the spray of the rock-beating surf.

And there lay the rider distorted and pale,
With the dew on his brow, and the rust on his mail:
And the tents were all silent, the banners alone,
The lances unlifted, the trumpet unblown.

And the widows of Ashur are loud in their wail,
And the idols are broke in the temple of Baal;
And the might of the Gentile, unsmote by the sword,
Hath melted like snow in the glance of the Lord!

GEORGE GORDON, LORD BYRON

This story from II Kings 19:32–36 tells how the Lord smote the Assyrians with a plague and saved the children of Israel from destruction by the worshipers of Baal.

JAMIE DOUGLAS

I was a lady of high renown
   As lived in the north countrie;
I was a lady of high renown
   Whan Earl Douglas loved me.

Whan we cam through Glasgow toun,
   We war a comely sight to see;
My gude lord in velvet green,
   And I mysel in cramasie.

Whan we cam to Douglas toun,
   We war a fine sight to behold;
My gude lord in cramasie,
   And I myself in shining gold.

Whan that my auld son was born,
   And set upon the nurse's knee,
I was as happy a woman as eer was born,
   And my gude lord he loved me.

But oh, an my young son was born,
   And set upon the nurse's knee,
And I myself war dead and gane,
   For a maid again I'll never be!

There cam a man into this house,
   And Jamie Lockhart was his name,
And it was told to my gude lord
   That I was in the bed wi him.

There cam anither to this house,
   And a bad friend he was to me;
He put Jamie's shoon below my bed-stock,
   And bade my gude lord come and see.

O wae be unto thee, Blackwood,
	And ae an ill death may ye dee!
For ye was the first and the foremost man
	That parted my gude lord and me.

Whan my gude lord cam in my room,
	This grit falsehood for to see,
He turned about, and, wi a gloom,
	He straucht did tak farewell o me.

"O fare thee well, my once lovely maid!
	O fare thee well, once dear to me!
O fare thee well, my once lovely maid!
	For wi me again ye sall never be."

"Sit doun, sit doun, Jamie Douglas,
	Sit thee doun and dine wi me,
And I'll set thee on a chair of gold,
	And a silver towel on thy knee."

"Whan cockle-shells turn silver bells,
	And mussels they bud on a tree,
Whan frost and snaw turns fire to burn,
	Then I'll sit down and dine wi thee."

O wae be unto thee, Blackwood,
	And ae an ill death may ye dee!
Ye war the first and the foremost man
	That parted my gude lord and me.

Whan my father he heard word
	That my gude lord had forsaken me,
He sent fifty o his brisk dragoons
	To fesh me hame to my ain countrie.

That morning before I did go,
   My bonny palace for to leave,
I went into my gude lord's room,
   But alas! he wad na speak to me.

"Fare thee well, Jamie Douglas!
   Fare thee well, my ever dear to me!
Fare thee well, Jamie Douglas!
   Be kind to the three babes I've born to thee."

O WALY, WALY UP THE BANK

O waly, waly up the bank,
   And waly, waly down the brae,
And waly, waly yon burn-side,
   Where I and my love wont to gae.

I lean'd my back unto an aik,
   I thought it was a trusty tree,
But first it bow'd, and syne it brak,
   Sae my true-love did lightly me.

O waly, waly, but love be bonny
   A little time, while it is new,
But when 'tis auld it waxeth cauld,
   And fades away like morning dew.

O wherefore should I busk my head?
   Or wherefore should I kame my hair?
For my true-love has me forsook,
   And says he will never love me mair.

Now Arthur-Seat shall be my bed,
   The sheets shall neer be fyl'd by me;
Saint Anton's well shall be my drink,
   Since my true-love has forsaken me.

Martinmas wind, when wilt thou blaw,
   And shake the green leaves off the tree?
O gentle death, when wilt thou come?
   For of my life I am weary.

'Tis not the frost that freezes fell,
   Nor blowing snaw's inclemency;
'Tis not sic cauld that makes me cry,
   But my love's heart grown cauld to me.

When we came in by Glasgow town,
    We were a comely sight to see;
My love was cled in the black velvet,
    And I my sell in cramasie.

But had I wist, before I kiss'd,
    That love had been sae ill to win,
I'd locked my heart in a case of gold,
    And pin'd it with a silver pin.

Oh, oh, if my young babes were born,
    And set upon the nurse's knee,
And I my sell were dead and gane!
    For a maid again I'll never be.

WAILY, WAILY

When cockle shells turn silver bells
And mussels grow on every tree,
When blooms the rose 'neath wintry snows,
Then will my false love be true to me.

Oh, waily, waily, but love is bonny
A little while when it is new,
But when it's old, it groweth cold
And fades away like morning dew.

Oh, had I wist before I kissed
That love had been so ill to win,
I'd locked my heart in case of gold
And pinned it with a silver pin.

Oh waily, waily, but love is bonny
A little while when it is new,
But when it's old, it groweth cold
And fades away like morning dew.

In the second edition of Bishop Percy's *Reliques of Ancient English Poetry* (1767), there appeared that greatest of Scottish lyric laments for a lost love, "Waly, Waly, Gin Love be Bonny." The song is much earlier than Percy's collection of it, but almost two centuries after that date the Library of Congress was fortunate enough to record it from the singing of Eugenia (Blount) Anderson, wife of Professor Charles Anderson of Johns Hopkins University, who had acquired it orally in Georgia.—Duncan Emrich, *Folklore on the American Land*.

"Waily, Waily" (Woe, Woe) is the lament of Lady Douglas for her husband. The story is told in "Jamie Douglas" (pp. 62-64) and this heartbreaking song is often incorporated in the narrative ballad. I have chosen two versions of the lament, one English, one American.—H.P.

BY THE EXETER RIVER

"What is it you're mumbling, old Father, my Dad?
Come drink up your soup and I'll put you to bed."

"By the Exeter River, by the river, I said."

"Stop dreaming of rivers, old Father, my Dad,
Or save all your dreaming till you're tucked in bed."

"It was cold by the river. We came in a sled."

"It's colder to think of, old Father, my Dad,
Than the blankets and bolsters and pillows of bed."

"We took off his dress and the cap from his head."

"Undressed in winter, old Father, my Dad?
What could you be thinking? Let's get off to bed."

"And Sally, poor Sally I reckon is dead."

"Was she an old sweetheart, old Father, my Dad?
Now lean on my shoulder and come up to bed."

"We drowned your half-brother. I remember we did."

DONALD HALL

THE CULPRIT

The night my father got me
  His mind was not on me;
He did not plague his fancy
  To muse if I should be
  The son you see.

The day my mother bore me
  She was a fool and glad,
For all the pain I cost her,
  That she had borne the lad
  That borne she had.

My mother and my father
  Out of the light they lie;
The warrant would not find them,
  And here 'tis only I
  Shall hang so high.

Oh let not man remember
  The soul that God forgot,
But fetch the county kerchief
  And noose me in the knot,
  And I will rot.

For so the game is ended
  That should not have begun.
My father and my mother
  They had a likely son,
  And I have none.

A. E. HOUSMAN

EDWARD, EDWARD

"Why does your brand sae drop wi' blude,
    Edward, Edward?
Why does your brand sae drop wi' blude,
    And why sae sad gang ye, O?"—
"O I hae kill'd my hawk sae gude,
    Mither, mither;
O I hae kill'd my hawk sae gude,
    And I had nae mair but he, O."

"Your hawk's blude was never sae red,
    Edward, Edward;
Your hawk's blude was never sae red,
    My dear son, I tell thee, O."—
"O I hae kill'd my red-roan steed,
    Mither, mither;
O I hae kill'd my red-roan steed,
    That erst was sae fair and free, O."

"Your steed was auld, and ye hae got mair,
    Edward, Edward;
Your steed was auld, and ye hae got mair;
    Some other dule ye dree,[1] O."—
"O I hae kill'd my father dear,
    Mither, mither;
O I hae kill'd my father dear,
    Alas, and wae is me, O!"

[1] grief you suffer

"And whatten penance will ye dree for that,
    Edward, Edward?
Whatten penance will ye dree for that?
    My dear son, now tell me, O."—
"I'll set my feet in yonder boat,
    Mither, mither;
I'll set my feet in yonder boat,
    And I'll fare over the sea, O."

"And what will ye do wi' your tow'rs and your ha',
    Edward, Edward?
And what will ye do wi' your tow'rs and your ha',
    That were sae fair to see, O?"—
"I'll let them stand till they doun fa',
    Mither, mither;
I'll let them stand till they doun fa',
    For here never mair maun I be, O."

"And what will ye leave to your bairns and your wife,
    Edward, Edward?
And what will ye leave to your bairns and your wife,
    When ye gang owre the sea, O?"—
"The warld's room: let them beg through life,
    Mither, mither;
The warld's room: let them beg through life;
    For them never mair will I see, O."

"And what will ye leave to your ain mither dear,
    Edward, Edward?
And what will ye leave to your ain mither dear,
    My dear son, now tell me, O?"—
"The curse of hell frae me sall ye bear,
    Mither, mither;
The curse of hell frae me sall ye bear:
    Sic counsels ye gave to me, O!"

LORD RANDAL

"Wha you been, Lord Randal, my son?
Wha you been, my handsome young man?"
"I ha been at the greenwood; mother, mak my bed soon,
For I'm wearied wi huntin, and fain wad lie down."

"An wha met ye there, Lord Randal, my son?
An wha met you there, my handsome young man?"
"O I met wi my true-love; mother, mak my bed soon,
For I'm wearied wi huntin, and fain wad lie down."

"And what did she give you, Lord Randal, my son?
And what did she give you, my handsome young man?"
"Eels fried in a pan; mother, mak my bed soon,
For I'm wearied wi huntin, and fain wad lie down."

"And wha gat your leavins, Lord Randal, my son?
And wha gat your leavins, my handsome young man?"
"My hawks and my hounds; mother, mak my bed soon,
For I'm wearied wi huntin, and fain wad lie down."

"And what becam of them, Lord Randal, my son?
And what becam of them, my handsome young man?"
"They stretched their legs out an died; mother, mak my
    bed soon,
For I'm wearied wi huntin, and fain wad lie down."

"O I fear you are poisoned, Lord Randal, my son!
I fear you are poisoned, my handsome young man!"
"O yes, I am poisoned; mother, mak my bed soon,
For I'm sick at the heart, and I fain wad lie down."

"Lord Randal" exists in many versions both in England and in America.
My mother told of singing it in the 90's in New York.

"What d'ye leave to your mother, Lord Randal, my son?
What d'ye leave to your mother, my handsome young man?"
"Four and twenty milk kye; mother, mak my bed soon,
For I'm sick at the heart, and I fain wad lie down."

"What d'ye leave to your sister, Lord Randal, my son?
What d'ye leave to your sister, my handsome young man?"
"My gold and my silver; mother, mak my bed soon,
For I'm sick at the heart, and I fain wad lie down."

"What d'ye leave to your brother, Lord Randal, my son?
What d'ye leave to your brother, my handsome young man?"
"My houses and my lands; mother, mak my bed soon,
For I'm sick at the heart, and I fain wad lie down."

"What d'ye leave to your true-love, Lord Randal, my son?
What d'ye leave to your true-love, my handsome young
    man?"
"I leave her hell and fire; mother, mak my bed soon,
For I'm sick at the heart, and I fain wad lie down."

THE TWO SISTERS

There lived an old lord by the northern sea,
  Bow down,
There lived an old lord by the northern sea.

The boughs they bent to me.
There lived an old lord by the northern sea,

And he had daughters, one, two, three.
That will be true, true to my love,
Love and my love will be true to me.

A young man came a-courting there,
He took choice of the youngest there.

He gave this girl a beaver hat,
The oldest she thought much of that.

O sister, O sister, let's we walk out
To see the ships a-sailing about.

As they walked down the salty brim,
The oldest pushed the youngest in.

O sister, O sister, lend me your hand,
And I will give you my house and land.

I'll neither lend you my hand or glove,
But I will have your own true love.

A striking resemblance to "Binnorie," although the American
version has no supernatural happenings.

Down she sank and away she swam,
And into the miller's pond she ran.

The miller came out with his fish hook
And fished the fair maid out of the brook.

And it's off her finger took five gold rings,
And into the brook he pushed her again.

The miller was hung at his mill gate
For drowning of my sister Kate.

THE DEAR GIRL

"Pretty, say when
You will have tied your posies?
Pinks for the men,
And for the maids, moss-roses."

"I've told my score;
And yet I would apparel
One posy more
For leave-take and nonpareil;

"And when 'tis done
I will myself bestow it
On the breast of one
To whom I think I owe it:

"A quiet breast,
Which nothing now amazes,
Wearing a fancy vest
Of green sprigged o'er with daisies.

"Yes, 'tis for Dick;
I never had a fellow
With head so thick,
Nor curls so crisp and yellow.

"He sued in vain;
I counselled him with laughter
To end his pain
With a rope's-end and a rafter;

"And in despair
He perished at my bidding.
He too must wear
A breast-knot at my wedding."

SYLVIA TOWNSEND WARNER

from *A SHROPSHIRE LAD*

"Farewell to barn and stack and tree,
    Farewell to Severn shore.
Terence, look your last at me,
    For I come home no more.

"The sun burns on the half-mown hill,
    By now the blood is dried;
And Maurice amongst the hay lies still
    And my knife is in his side.

"My mother thinks us long away;
    'Tis time the field were mown.
She had two sons at rising day,
    To-night she'll be alone.

"And here's a bloody hand to shake,
    And oh, man, here's good-bye;
We'll sweat no more on scythe and rake,
    My bloody hands and I.

"I wish you strength to bring you pride,
    And a love to keep you clean,
And I wish you luck, come Lammastide,
    At racing on the green.

"Long for me the rick will wait,
    And long will wait the fold,
And long will stand the empty plate,
    And dinner will be cold."

A. E. HOUSMAN

THE BROTHER

O know you what I have done
To avenge our sister? She,
I thought, was wantoned with
By a man of levity:

And I lay in wait all day,
All day did I wait for him,
And dogged him to Bollard Head
When twilight dwindled dim,

And hurled him over the edge
And heard him fall below:
O would I were lying with him,
For the truth I did not know!

"O where's my husband?" she asked,
As evening wore away:
"Best you had one, forsooth,
But never had you!" I say.

"Yes, but I have!" says she,
"My Love made it up with me,
And we churched it yesterday
And mean to live happily."

And now I go in haste
To the Head, before she's aware,
To join him in death for the wrong
I've done them both out there!

THOMAS HARDY

THE MAID FREED FROM THE GALLOWS

"Slack your rope, hangs-a-man,
  O slack it for a while;
I think I see my father coming,
  Riding many a mile."
"O father, have you brought me gold?
  Or have you paid my fee?
Or have you come to see me hanging
  On the gallows-tree?"
"I have not brought you gold;
  I have not paid your fee;
But I have come to see you hanging
  On the gallows-tree."

"Slack your rope, hangs-a-man,
  O slack it for a while;
I think I see my mother coming, [1]
  Riding many a mile."
"O mother, have you brought me gold?
  Or have you paid my fee?
Or have you come to see me hanging
  On the gallows-tree?"
"I have not brought you gold;
  I have not paid your fee;
But I have come to see you hanging
  On the gallows-tree."

[1] And so on for brother, sister, aunt, uncle, cousin, etc.

American

"Slack your rope, hangs-a-man,
    O slack it for a while;
I think I see my true-love coming,
    Riding many a mile."
"O true-love, have you brought me gold?
    Or have you paid my fee?
Or have you come to see me hanging
    On the gallows-tree?"
"Yes, I have brought you gold;
    Yes, I have paid your fee;
Nor have I come to see you hanging
    On the gallows-tree."

GEORGIE

As I walked over London Bridge,
One misty morning early,
I heard some fair young maiden say,
"Lord, spare me the life of Georgie."

"Go saddle me up my milk white steed,
And bridle them so gaily.
Then I'll ride away to the king's high court,
And plead for the life of Georgie."

She rode all day and she rode all night,
Till she was wet and weary.
Then combing back her long yellow hair,
She plead for the life of Georgie.

She pulled out a purse all filled with gold,
Just like you've never seen many.
And she said, "Young lawyers fee yourselves,
And plead for the life of Georgie."

But Georgie rode up and he plead for himself.
He says, "I never murdered any.
But I stole sixteen of the king's best steeds
And sold them in Romany."

Then the oldest lawyer at the bar
Says, "George, I'm sorry for you.
But your own confession condemns you to die,
May the Lord have mercy upon you."

American

As Georgie was a-walkin' through the streets
He bid farewell to many
Then he bid farewell to his own true love
Which grieved him worst than any.

If I was over on yonder hill
Where kisses I've had a-plenty,
With my sword and my pistol by my side
I'd fight for the life of Georgie.

Georgie was hanged with a golden cord,
Just like you've never seen many.
For he was a member of the royal race,
And loved by a virtuous lady.

THE TWA CORBIES

As I was walking all alane,
I heard twa corbies making a mane;
The tane unto the t'other say,
"Where sall we gang and dine to-day?"

"In behint yon auld fail [1] dyke,
I wot there lies a new slain knight;
And naebody kens that he lies there,
But his hawk, his hound, and lady fair.

"His hound is to the hunting game,
His hawk to fetch the wild-fowl hame,
His lady's ta'en another mate,
So we may mak our dinner sweet.

"Ye'll sit on his white hause-bane,
And I'll pike out his bonny blue een;
Wi ae lock o his gowden hair
We'll theek our nest when it grows bare.

"Mony a one for him makes mane,
But nane sall ken where he is gane;
Oer his white banes, when they are bare,
The wind sall blaw for evermair."

[1] turf

THE THREE RAVENS

There were three rauens sat on a tree,
   Downe a downe, hay downe, hay downe
There were three rauens sat on a tree,
   With a downe
There were three rauens sat on a tree,
They were as blacke as they might be.
   With a downe derrie, derrie, derrie, downe, downe

The one of them said to his mate,
"Where shall we our breakefast take?"

"Downe in yonder greene field,
There lies a knight slain vnder his shield.

"His hounds they lie downe at his feete,
So well they can their master keepe.

"His haukes they flie so eagerly,
There's no fowle dare him come nie."

Downe there comes a fallow doe,
As great with yong as she might goe.

She lift vp his bloudy hed,
And kist his wounds that were so red.

She got him vp vpon her backe,
And carried him to earthen lake.

She buried him before the prime,
She was dead herselfe ere euen-song time.

God send euery gentleman,
Such haukes, such hounds, and such a leman.[1]

[1] sweetheart or wife

SIR PATRICK SPENS

I. *The Sailing*

The king sits in Dunfermline town
　　Drinking the blude-red wine;
"O whare will I get a skeely [1] skipper
　　To sail this new ship o' mine?"

O up and spak an eldern knight,
　　Sat at the king's right knee:
"Sir Patrick Spens is the best sailor
　　That ever sail'd the sea."

Our king has written a braid letter,
　　And seal'd it with his hand,
And sent it to Sir Patrick Spens,
　　Was walking on the strand.

"To Noroway, to Noroway,
　　To Noroway o'er the faem;
The king's daughter o' Noroway,
　　'Tis thou must bring her hame."

The first word that Sir Patrick read
　　So loud, loud laugh'd he;
The neist word that Sir Patrick read
　　The tear blinded his e'e.

"O wha is this has done this deed
　　And tauld the king o' me,
To send us out, at this time o' year,
　　To sail upon the sea?

---

[1] skillful

"Be it wind, be it weet, be it hail, be it sleet,
    Our ship must sail the faem;
The king's daughter o' Noroway,
    'Tis we must fetch her hame."

They hoysed their sails on Monenday morn
    Wi' a' the speed they may;
They hae landed in Noroway
    Upon a Wodensday.

II. *The Return*

"Mak ready, mak ready, my merry men a'!
    Our gude ship sails the morn."—
"Now ever alack, my master dear,
    I fear a deadly storm.

"I saw the new moon late yestreen
    Wi' the auld moon in her arm;
And if we gang to sea, master,
    I fear we'll come to harm."

They hadna sail'd a league, a league,
    A league but barely three,
When the lift [2] grew dark, and the wind blew loud,
    And gurly grew the sea.

The ankers brak, and the topmast lap,[3]
    It was sic a deadly storm:
And the waves cam owre the broken ship
    Till a' her sides were torn.

[2] sky   [3] sprang

"O where will I get a gude sailor
   To tak' my helm in hand,
Till I get up to the tall topmast
   To see if I can spy land?"—

"O here am I, a sailor gude,
   To tak' the helm in hand,
Till you go up to the tall topmast,
   But I fear you'll ne'er spy land."

He hadna gane a step, a step,
   A step but barely ane,
When a bolt flew out of our goodly ship,
   And the saut sea it came in.

"Go fetch a web o' the silken claith,
   Another o' the twine,
And wap [4] them into our ship's side,
   And let nae the sea come in."

They fetch'd a web o' the silken claith,
   Another o' the twine,
And they wapp'd them round that gude ship
   But still the sea came in.

O laith, laith were our gude Scots lords
   To wet their cork-heel'd shoon;
But lang or a' the play was play'd
   They wat their hats aboon.

And mony was the feather bed
   That flatter'd [5] on the faem;
And mony was the gude lord's son
   That never mair cam hame.

[4] wrap   [5] tossed afloat

O lang, lang may the ladies sit,
    Wi' their fans into their hand,
Before they see Sir Patrick Spens
    Come sailing to the strand!

And lang, lang may the maidens sit
    Wi' their gowd kames [6] in their hair,
A-waiting for their ain dear loves!
    For them they'll see nae mair.

Half-owre, half-owre to Aberdour,
    'Tis fifty fathoms deep;
And there lies gude Sir Patrick Spens,
    Wi' the Scots lords at his feet!

[6] combs

BONNY GEORGE CAMPBELL

Hie upon Hielands,
    And laigh [1] upon Tay,
Bonny George Campbell
    Rade out on a day:
Saddled and bridled,
    Sae gallant to see,
Hame cam' his gude horse,
    But never cam' he.

Down ran his auld mither,
    Greetin' [2] fu' sair;
Out ran his bonny bride,
    Reaving [3] her hair;
"My meadow lies green,
    And my corn is unshorn,
My barn is to bigg,[4]
    And my babe is unborn."

Saddled and bridled
    And booted rade he;
A plume in his helmet,
    A sword at his knee;
But toom [5] cam' his saddle
    A' bluidy to see,
O hame cam' his gude horse,
    But never cam' he!

[1] low   [2] crying   [3] tearing
[4] build   [5] empty

THE BONNY EARL OF MURRAY

Ye Highlands and ye Lawlands,
  O where hae ye been?
They hae slain the Earl of Murray,
  And hae laid him on the green.

Now wae be to thee, Huntley!
  And whairfore did ye sae!
I bade you bring him wi' you,
  But forbade you him to slay.

He was a braw gallant,
  And he rid at the ring;
And the bonny Earl of Murray,
  O he might hae been a king!

He was a braw gallant,
  And he play'd at the ba';
And the bonny Earl of Murray
  Was the flower amang them a'!

He was a braw gallant,
  And he play'd at the gluve;
And the bonny Earl of Murray,
  O he was the Queen's luve!

O lang will his Lady
  Look owre the Castle Downe,
Ere she see the Earl of Murray
  Come sounding through the town!

SPRINGFIELD MOUNTAIN

On Springfield Mountain there did dwell
A likely youth was known full well;
Timothy Myrick was his name,
Lieutenant Myrick's only son.

On Friday morning he did go
Down to the meadow for to mow;
He mowed and mowed around the field
Till a poisonous serpent bit his heel.

When he received his deathly wound
He laid his scythe down on the ground;
For to return was his intent
Crying out loud long as he went.

His cries were heard both near and far,
But no friend to him did appear;
They thought he did some workman call,
And so poor boy alone did fall.

Day being done, now, and night coming on,
The father went to seek his son,
And soon his only son he found
Cold as a stone, dead on the ground.

He took him up and bore him home,
And all the time did cry and mourn,
Saying "I heard, but did not come,
And now I'm left alone to mourn."

'Twas the seventh of August in seventeen sixty-one,
That this sad accident was done;
Let this a warning be to all,
To be prepared when God doth call.

American

&۔ 91

MARY HAMILTON

Word's gane to the kitchen,
   And word's gane to the ha',
That Mary Hamilton gangs wi' bairn
   To the highest Stewart of a'.

He's courted her in the kitchen,
   He's courted her in the ha',
He's courted her in the laigh [1] cellar,
   And that was warst of a'.

She's tyed it in her apron
   And she's thrown it in the sea;
Says, sink ye, swim ye, bonny wee babe!
   You'll neer get mair o me.

Down then cam the auld queen,
   Goud tassels tying her hair;
"O Marie, where's the bonny wee babe
   That I heard greet [2] sae sair?"

"There was never a babe intill my room,
   As little designs to be;
It was but a touch o my sair side,
   Come o'er my fair bodie."

"O Marie put on your robes o black,
   Or else your robes o brown,
For ye maun gang wi me the night,
   To see fair Edinbro town."

[1] low   [2] cry

Mary Hamilton, a lady-in-waiting to Mary, Queen of Scots, was said to have borne a child to Lord Darnley, the Queen's husband.

"I winna put on my robes o black,
 Nor yet my robes o brown;
But I'll put on my robes o white,
 To see fair Edinbro town."

When she gaed up the Cannogate,
 She laughed loud laughters three;
But whan she cam down the Cannogate
 The tear blinded her ee.

When she gaed up the Parliament stair,
 The heel cam aff her shee;
And lang or she cam down again
 She was condemned to dee.

When she cam down the Cannogate,
 The Cannogate sae free,
Many a lady lookd owre her window,
 Weeping for this ladie.

"Ye need nae weep for me," she says,
 "Ye need nae weep for me;
For had I not slain mine own sweet babe,
 This death I wadna dee.

"Bring me a bottle of wine," she says,
 "The best that ee ye hae,
That I may drink to my weil-wishers,
 And they may drink to me.

"Here's a health to the jolly sailors,
 That sail upon the main;
Let them never let on to my father and mother
 But what I'm coming hame.

"Here's a health to the jolly sailors,
    That sail upon the sea;
Let them never let on to my father and mother
    That I cam here to dee.

"O little did my mother think
    The day she cradled me,
What lands I was to travel through,
    What death I was to dee.

"O little did my father think
    The day he held up me,
What lands I was to travel through,
    What death I was to dee.

"Last night I washd the queen's feet,
    And gently laid her down;
And a' the thanks I've gotten the nicht
    To be hangd in Edinbro town!

"Last nicht there was four Maries,
    The nicht there'll be but three;
There was Mary Seton, and Marie Beton,
    And Marie Carmichael, and me."

THE DUAL SITE

To my twin who lives in a cruel country
　　I wrote a letter at last;
For my bones creaked out in our long silence
　　That seven years had passed,

Seven whole years since he and I
　　By word or token exchanged
The message I dare not do without:
　　That still we are not estranged,

Though I watch figures in a city office
　　And he the waves of the sea,
Keeping no count since he hardly cares
　　What happens to him or to me;

Since to names and numbers he closed his head
　　When, children still, we were parted,
Chose birth and death for his calendar,
　　But leaves the dates uncharted,

Being one who forgets what I remember,
　　Who knows what I do not,
Who has learnt the ways of otter and raven
　　While I've grown polyglot.

Lately I found a cactus in flower
　　And feared for his apple-trees,
Dozed in the club and saw his cattle
　　Drag with a foul disease,

And my bones grown stiff with leaning and lying
　　Cried out that I'll labour in vain
Till I help my twin to rebuild his hovel
　　That's open to wind and rain.

So I sent him a note, expecting no answer,
    And a cheque he'd never cash,
For I knew he was one who'd smile if he heard
    His own roof come down with a crash,

But above the porpoise-leaping bay
    Where ploughshare fin and tail
Cut furrows the foam-flecked sea fills up
    He'd stand in the swishing gale,

Calm as the jackdaws that nest in crannies
    And no more prone to doubt,
With gull and cormorant perched on the rocks
    Would wait the weather out.

Yet he wrote by return: "Have no fear for your dwelling
    Though dry-rot gnaws at the floors;
Only lighten their load of marble and metal,
    Keep clear the corridors,

Move out the clocks that clutter your study,
    And the years will leave you alone:
Every frame I know of lasts long enough,
    Though but cardboard, wood or bone.

And spare me your nightmares, brother, I beg you,
    They make my daemons laugh,
They scare the spirits that rarely will visit
    A man with no wand or staff,

With no symbol, no book and no formula,
    No lore to aid him at all,
Who wherever he walks must find the image
    That holds his mentors in thrall.

But your waking cares put down on paper
    For me to give to the wind,
That the seed may fall and the dry leaf crumble,
    Not a wisp be left behind

Of the tangle that hides the dual site
    Where even you and I
Still may meet again and together build
    One house before we die."

MICHAEL HAMBURGER

BALLAD OF THE MAN WHO'S GONE

No money to bury him.
The relief gave Forty-Four.
The undertaker told 'em,
You'll need Sixty more

For a first-class funeral,
A hearse and two cars—
And maybe your friends'll
Send some flowers.

His wife took a paper
And went around.
Everybody that gave something
She put 'em down.

She raked up a Hundred
For her man that was dead.
His buddies brought flowers.
A funeral was had.

A minister preached—
And charged Five
To bless him dead
And praise him alive.

Now that he's buried—
God rest his soul—
Reckon there's no charge
For graveyard mold.

I wonder what makes
A funeral so high?
A poor man ain't got
No business to die.

LANGSTON HUGHES

THE ARREST OF OSCAR WILDE
AT THE CADOGAN HOTEL

He sipped at a weak hock and seltzer
  As he gazed at the London skies
Through the Nottingham lace of the curtains
  Or was it his bees-winged eyes?

To the right and before him Pont Street
  Did tower in her new built red,
As hard as the morning gaslight
  That shone on his unmade bed.

"I want some more hock in my seltzer,
  And Robbie, please give me your hand—
Is this the end or beginning?
  How can I understand?

"So you've brought me the latest *Yellow Book*:
  And Buchan has got in it now:
Approval of what is approved of
  Is as false as a well-kept vow.

"More hock, Robbie—where is the seltzer?
  Dear boy, pull again at the bell!
They are all little better than *cretins*,
  Though this *is* the Cadogan Hotel.

"One astrakhan coat is at Willis's—
  Another one's at the Savoy:
Do fetch my morocco portmanteau,
  And bring them on later, dear boy."

A thump, and a murmur of voices—
   ("Oh why must they make such a din?")
As the door of the bedroom swung open
   And TWO PLAIN CLOTHES POLICEMEN came in:

"Mr. Woilde, we 'ave come for tew take yew
   Where felons and criminals dwell:
We must ask yew tew leave with us quoietly
   For this *is* the Cadogan Hotel."

He rose, and he put down *The Yellow Book*.
   He staggered—and, terrible-eyed,
He brushed past the palms on the staircase
   And was helped to a hansom outside.

JOHN BETJEMAN

THE IMPULSE

It was too lonely for her there,
   And too wild,
And since there were but two of them,
   And no child,

And work was little in the house,
   She was free,
And followed where he furrowed field,
   Or felled tree.

She rested on a log and tossed
   The fresh chips,
With a song only to herself
   On her lips.

And once she went to break a bough
   Of black alder.
She strayed so far she scarcely heard
   When he called her—

And didn't answer—didn't speak—
   Or return.
She stood, and then she ran and hid
   In the fern.

He never found her, though he looked
   Everywhere,
And he asked at her mother's house
   Was she there.

Sudden and swift and light as that
   The ties gave,
And he learned of finalities
   Besides the grave.

                                        ROBERT FROST

ॐ *101*

THE GOLDEN VANITY

Now Jack he had a ship in the North Counterie,
She goes by the name of the Golden Vanity.
I'm afraid she'll be taken by some Turkish galléy
As she sails on the Lowlands, Lowlands Low,
As she sails on the Lowlands Low.

Then up spoke the little saucy cabin-boy
Saying, Master, what will you give me if I will her destroy?
It's I will give thee gold and I will give thee store
And you shall have my daughter when I returns on shore
If you sink her in the Lowlands, Lowlands Low,
If you sink her in the Lowlands Low.

This boy bent his breast and he jumped in,
This boy bent his breast and away he did swim.
He swum till he came to some Turkish galléy
As she sails on the Lowlands, Lowlands Low,
As she sails on the Lowlands Low.

This boy had an auger bored nine holes at once,
He bored a hole at the bottom of the slew,
Where some was playing cards and some was playing dice
And he let the water in and dazzled all their eyes,
And he sunk them in the Lowlands, Lowlands Low,
And he sunk them in the Lowlands Low.

This boy bent his breast and he jumped in,
This boy bent his breast and away back he swum,
He swum till he came to some starboard side
Saying, Master, take me up, or else I shall die,
As he sunk them in the Lowlands, Lowlands Low,
As he sunk them in the Lowlands Low.

Then they took him up and laid him on the starboard side,
They laid him on the deck and then he did die.
They wrappéd him up in an old cow's hide
And they sunk him in the Lowlands, Lowlands Low,
And they sunk him in the Lowlands Low.

THE GREEN WILLOW TREE

There was a ship a-sailing off North America,
   Crying, O, 't is lonesome in the Lowlands low
There was a ship a-sailing off North America,
And she went by the name of the Green Willow Tree.
   As we're sailing in the Lowlands low

She had n't been on sea for more than weeks three,
Until she was overtaken by the Turkish Revelee.

Up spoke the Captain, saying, "Who will it be,
To go and destroy the Turkish Revelee?"

Up steps the cabin-boy, saying, "What will you give me,
If I overtake her and destroy all her crew?"

"I will give you gold and I will give you fee,
Likewise, my eldest daughter your wedded bride shall be."

He fell upon his breast and away swam he,
He swam till he came to the Turkish Revelee.

He had a tool just fitted for the use,
He bored in a hole and let in a sluice.

Some were playing cards and some were playing checks,
And the first thing they knew they were in water to their
    necks.

He fell upon his breast and away swam he,
Swam till he came to the Green Willow Tree.

Saying, "Captain, O Captain, won't you take me on board,
And be as good to me as your word?"

"Oh no, sir, oh no, sir, not take you on board,
Nor be as good to you as my word."

He fell upon his breast and down sank he,
Bidding adieu to the Green Willow Tree.

BARBARA ALLEN'S CRUELTY

In Scarlet Town, where I was bound,
   There was a fair maid dwelling,
Whom I had chosen to be my own,
   And her name it was Barbara Allen.

All in the merry month of May,
   When green leaves they was springing,
This young man on his death-bed lay,
   For the love of Barbara Allen.

He sent his man unto her then,
   To the town where she was dwelling:
"You must come to my master dear,
   If your name be Barbara Allen.

"For death is printed in his face,
   And sorrow's in him dwelling,
And you must come to my master dear,
   If your name be Barbara Allen."

"If death be printed in his face,
   And sorrow's in him dwelling,
Then little better shall he be
   For bonny Barbara Allen."

So slowly, slowly she got up,
   And so slowly she came to him,
And all she said when she came there,
   Young man, I think you are a dying.

He turned his face unto her then:
    "If you be Barbara Allen,
My dear," said he, "come pity me,
    As on my death-bed I am lying."

"If on your death-bed you be lying,
    What is that to Barbara Allen?
I cannot keep you from [your] death;
    So farewell," said Barbara Allen.

He turned his face unto the wall,
    And death came creeping to him:
"Then adieu, adieu, and adieu to all,
    And adieu to Barbara Allen!"

And as she was walking on a day,
    She heard the bell a ringing,
And it did seem to ring to her
    "Unworthy Barbara Allen."

She turned herself round about,
    And she spy'd the corps a coming:
"Lay down, lay down the corps of clay,
    That I may look upon him."

And all the while she looked on,
    So loudly she lay laughing,
While all her friends cry'd [out] amain,
    "Unworthy Barbara Allen!"

When he was dead, and laid in grave,
    Then death came creeping to she:
"O mother, mother, make my bed,
    For his death hath quite undone me.

"A hard-hearted creature that I was,
    To slight one that lovd me so dearly;
I wish I had been more kinder to him,
    The time of his life when he was near me."

So this maid she then did dye,
    And desired to be buried by him,
And repented her self before she dy'd,
    That ever she did deny him.

BARBARA ELLEN

In Scotland I was bred and born,
  In London was my dwelling;
I fell in love with a pretty maid,
  Her name was Barbara Ellen.

I courted her for months and weeks,
  Hoping that I might gain her;
Although she solemnly replied,
  No man on earth should have her.

'T was in the merry month of May,
  The flowers and trees were swaying;
A young man on his death bed lay
  For the love of Barbara Ellen.

He sent his servant to his home,
  To the place of Barbara's dwelling;
"My master he doth call on thee,
  If thy name be Barbara Ellen."

Slowly she put on her things,
  And slowly she went to him;
And all she said, when she got there,
  Was, "Young man, I think you're dying.

"And if it be for love of me
  You're on your death bed lying,
But little better would you be
  For the love of Barbara Ellen.

An American "Barbara Allen"

"Do you remember last New Year's Eve,
    Way down at yonder dwelling,
You drank a toast to all around
    And slighted Barbara Ellen?"

He turned his pale face to the wall,
    As death was creeping on him:
"Farewell, farewell to all around,
    And adieu to Barbara Ellen."

As she was walking in the fields,
    She heard the bells a-tolling;
And every toll it seemed to say,
    "O cruel Barbara Ellen!"

As she was walking in the street,
    She saw the corpse a-coming:
"Lay down, lay down that corpse," she cried,
    "That I may gaze upon him.

"Mother, mother, make my bed,
    Make it soft and narrow;
For Willie was buried for me to-day,
    And I'll die for him to-morrow."

One was buried in the high churchyard,
    The other in the choir;
On one there grew a red rose bush,
    On the other there grew a brier.

They grew and they grew to the high steeple top,
    Till they could grow no higher;
And there they locked in a true-lover's knot,
    For true lovers to admire.

THE BAILIFF'S DAUGHTER
OF ISLINGTON

There was a youth, and a well belovd youth,
    And he was a esquire's son,
He loved the bayliff's daughter dear,
    That lived in Islington.

She was coy, and she would not believe
    That he did love her so,
No, nor at any time she would
    Any countenance to him show.

But when his friends did understand
    His fond and foolish mind,
They sent him up to fair London,
    An apprentice for to bind.

And when he had been seven long years,
    And his love he had not seen,
"Many a tear have I shed for her sake
    When she little thought of me."

All the maids of Islington
    Went forth to sport and play;
All but the bayliff's daughter dear;
    She secretly stole away.

She put off her gown of gray,
    And put on her puggish attire;
She's up to fair London gone,
    Her true-love to require.

As she went along the road,
    The weather being hot and dry,
There was she aware of her true-love,
    At length came riding by.

She stept to him, as red as any rose,
    And took him by the bridle-ring:
"I pray you, kind sir, give me one penny,
    To ease my weary limb."

"I prithee, sweetheart, canst thou tell me
    Where that thou wast born?"
"At Islington, kind sir," said she,
    "Where I have had many a scorn."

"I prithee, sweetheart, canst thou tell me
    Whether thou dost know
The bailiff's daughter of Islington?"
    "She's dead, sir, long ago."

"Then will I sell my goodly steed,
    My saddle and my bow;
I will into some far countrey,
    Where no man doth me know."

"O stay, O stay, thou goodly youth!
    She's alive, she is not dead;
Here she standeth by thy side,
    And is ready to be thy bride."

"O farewel grief, and welcome joy,
    Ten thousand times and more!
For now I have seen my own true-love,
    That I thought I should have seen no more."

LOCHINVAR

O, young Lochinvar is come out of the west,
Through all the wide Border his steed was the best;
And save his good broadsword he weapons had none,
He rode all unarmed, and he rode all alone.
So faithful in love, and so dauntless in war,
There never was knight like the young Lochinvar.

He stayed not for brake, and he stopped not for stone,
He swam the Eske river where ford there was none;
But ere he alighted at Netherby gate,
The bride had consented, the gallant came late:
For a laggard in love, and a dastard in war,
Was to wed the fair Ellen of brave Lochinvar.

So boldly he entered the Netherby Hall,
Among bride's-men, and kinsmen, and brothers, and all:
Then spoke the bride's father, his hand on his sword,
(For the poor craven bridegroom said never a word)
"O come ye in peace here, or come ye in war,
Or to dance at our bridal, young Lord Lochinvar?"

"I long wooed your daughter, my suit you denied;—
Love swells like the Solway, but ebbs like its tide—
And now am I come, with this lost love of mine,
To lead but one measure, drink one cup of wine.
There are maidens in Scotland more lovely by far,
That would gladly be bride to the young Lochinvar."

The bride kissed the goblet: the knight took it up,
He quaffed off the wine, and he threw down the cup.
She looked down to blush, and she looked up to sigh,
With a smile on her lips, and a tear in her eye.
He took her soft hand, ere her mother could bar,—
"Now tread we a measure!" said the young Lochinvar.

So stately his form and so lovely her face,
That never a hall such a galliard did grace;
While her mother did fret, and her father did fume,
And the bridegroom stood dangling his bonnet and plume;
And the bride-maidens whispered, " 'Twere better by far,
To have matched our fair cousin with young Lochinvar."

One touch to her hand, and one word in her ear,
When they reached the hall-door, and the charger stood near;
So light to the croup the fair lady he swung,
So light to the saddle before her he sprung!
"She is won! we are gone, over bank, bush, and scaur;
They'll have fleet steeds that follow," quoth young
        Lochinvar.

There was mounting 'mong Graemes of the Netherby clan;
Forsters, Fenwicks, and Musgraves, they rode and they ran:
There was racing and chasing on Cannobie Lee,
But the lost bride of Netherby ne'er did they see.
So daring in love, and so dauntless in war,
Have ye e'er heard of gallant like young Lochinvar?

SIR WALTER SCOTT

A wandering minstrel I

❧ BROADSIDES
& SATIRES

HAVE OVER THE WATER TO FLORIDA

Have over the water to Floryda,
  Farewell, gay Lundon, nowe;
Throwe long delés by land and sese
  I am brawght, I cannot tell howe,
To Plymwoorthe towne, in a thredbare gowne,
  And mony never (a) dele.
        With hy! wunnot a wallet do well?

And as I walked towards poles,
  I met a frend of myne
Who toke me by the hand and sayde
  "Cum drynk a pynt of wyne;
Wher yow shall here suche news, I fere,
  As yow abrode wyll compell."
        With hy!

"Have yow not hard of Floryda,
  A coontré far be west?
Wher savage pepell planted are
  By nature and by hest,
Who in the mold fynd glysterynge gold,
  And yt for tryfels sell,
        With hy!

Ye, all alonge the water syde,
  Where yt doth eb and flowe,
Are turkeyse found, and where also
  Do perles in oysteres growe;
And on the land do cedars stand,
  Whose bewty do excell.
With hy! tryksy trym, go tryksy, wunnot a wallet do well?

FROM "WESTERN STAR"

"Oh, have you heard the gallant news,
New-brought across the foam
Of Captain Newport's noble cruise
Whence he hath just come home?
He brings from far Virginia
Rare tidings, it is clear.
So, masters, pass the bowl about
And merrily give ear."

The little secretary looked at the lines,
Pursing his lips. His eyes traveled farther on.
Vile verse, but it would do for the ballad-singers
And they got people talking. He cleared his throat
While the starveling poet glowered and bit his thumbs.
Aye, this was more to the matter.

"There's heaps of gold and precious stones
So easy to be found
That every man may justly say
'This is Tom Tiddler's Ground.'
And, though most cruel salvages
Like dragons guard the den,
Their petty bows and heathen shows
Shall ne'er daunt Englishmen."

The little secretary smiled in his hand.
It would draw them—aye—the gold and the precious stones.
But the "cruel salvages" might be softened a whit.
Say "painted"—aye, "the poor painted salvages."
That sounded better. He glanced at the last verse.

In these lines, Benét describes the making of a ballad designed to attract
English settlers to the colony of Virginia.

"So, all you brave inquiring hearts
And every gallant soul,
Rise up and cry amain with me
'Virginia is the goal!'
For there we'll cast our cares away
And there our fortunes stand
And we shall live like golden men
In fair Virginia's land!"

He winced a little, reading the doggerel,
But it would do for the groundlings—it would serve
With a dozen bawling voices to sound it out.
He pushed a half-a-dozen coins across to the poet,
"Aye—'twill do," he said, with a patronizing smile,
"With the change of a word or two. You'll hear it sung."

STEPHEN VINCENT BENÉT

THE BOLD PEDLAR AND ROBIN HOOD

There chanced to be a pedlar bold,
  A pedlar bold he chanced to be;
He rolled his pack all on his back,
  And he came tripping oer the lee.
    Down a down a down a down,
      Down a down a down

By chance he met two troublesome blades,
  Two troublesome blades they chanced to be;
The one of them was bold Robin Hood,
  And the other was Little John so free.

"O pedlar, pedlar, what is in thy pack?
  Come speedilie and tell to me:"
"I've several suits of the gay green silks,
  And silken bow-strings two or three."

"If you have several suits of the gay green silk,
  And silken bow-strings two or three,
Then it's by my body," cries Little John,
  "One half your pack shall belong to me."

"O nay, o nay," says the pedlar bold,
  "O nay, o nay, that never can be;
For there's never a man from fair Nottingham
  Can take one half my pack from me."

Then the pedlar he pulled off his pack,
  And put it a little below his knee,
Saying, If you do move me one perch from this,
  My pack and all shall gang with thee.

Then Little John he drew his sword,
   The pedlar by his pack did stand;
They fought until they both did sweat,
   Till he cried, Pedlar, pray hold your hand!

Then Robin Hood he was standing by,
   And he did laugh most heartilie;
Saying, I could find a man, of a smaller scale,
   Could thrash the pedlar and also thee.

"Go you try, master," says Little John,
   "Go you try, master, most speedilie,
Or by my body," says Little John,
   "I am sure this night you will not know me."

Then Robin Hood he drew his sword,
   And the pedlar by his pack did stand;
They fought till the blood in streams did flow,
   Till he cried, Pedlar, pray hold your hand!

Pedlar, pedlar, what is thy name?
   Come speedilie and tell to me:
"My name! my name I neer will tell,
   Till both your names you have told to me."

"The one of us is bold Robin Hood,
   And the other Little John so free:"
"Now," says the pedlar, "it lays to my good will,
   Whether my name I chuse to tell to thee.

"I am Gamble Gold of the gay green woods,
   And travelled far beyond the sea;
For killing a man in my father's land
   From my country I was forced to flee."

"If you are Gamble Gold of the gay green woods,
    And travelled far beyond the sea,
You are my mother's own sister's son;
    What nearer cousins then can we be?"

They sheathed their swords with friendly words,
    So merrilie they did agree;
They went to a tavern, and there they dined,
    And bottles cracked most merrilie.

JESSE JAMES

It was on a Wednesday night, the moon was shining bright,
    They robbed the Glendale train.
And the people they did say, for many miles away,
    'Twas the outlaws Frank and Jesse James.

Refrain:
    Jesse had a wife to mourn all her life,
        The children they are brave.
    'Twas a dirty little coward shot Mister Howard,
        And laid Jesse James in his grave.

It was Robert Ford, the dirty little coward,
    I wonder how he does feel,
For he ate of Jesse's bread and he slept in Jesse's bed,
    Then he laid Jesse James in his grave.

Refrain

It was his brother Frank that robbed the Gallatin bank,
    And carried the money from the town.
It was in this very place that they had a little race,
    For they shot Captain Sheets to the ground.

Refrain

They went to the crossing not very far from there,
    And there they did the same;
And the agent on his knees he delivered up the keys
    To the outlaws Frank and Jesse James.

Refrain

An American Robin Hood

৯ *123*

It was on a Saturday night, Jesse was at home
    Talking to his family brave,
When the thief and the coward, little Robert Ford,
    Laid Jesse James in his grave.

Refrain

How people held their breath when they heard of Jesse's
        death,
    And wondered how he ever came to die
'Twas one of the gang, dirty Robert Ford,
    That shot Jesse James on the sly.

Refrain

Jesse went to his rest with his hand on his breast.
    The devil will be upon his knee.
He was born one day in the county of Clay,
    And came from a solitary race.

Refrain

BRENNAN ON THE MOOR

It's of a famous highwayman a story I will tell,
His name was Willie Brennan and in Ireland he did dwell,
And on the Kilworth mountains he commenced his wild
  career,
And many a wealthy gentleman before him shook with fear.
  Brennan on the Moor, Brennan on the Moor,
  A brave undaunted robber bold was Brennan on the Moor.

A brace of loaded pistols he carried night and day,
He never robbed a poor man upon the king's highway,
But what he'd taken from the rich, like Turpin and Black
  Bess,
He always did divide it with the widow in distress.

One night he robbed a packman by the name of Pedlar Bawn,
They travelled on together till day began to dawn.
The pedlar seeing his money gone, likewise his watch and
  chain,
He at once encountered Brennan and he robbed him back
  again.

One day upon the highway, as Willie he went down,
He met the Mayor of Cashel a mile outside the town.
The Mayor he knew his features. "I think, young man,"
  said he,
"Your name is Willie Brennan, you must come along with
  me."

As Brennan's wife had gone to town, provisions for to buy,
And when she saw her Willie she began to weep and cry.
He says, "Give me that tenpenny." As soon as Willie spoke,
She handed him a blunderbuss from underneath her cloak.

An Irish Robin Hood

Then with his loaded blunderbuss, the truth I will unfold,
He made the Mayor to tremble, and robbed him of his gold.
One hundred pounds was offered for his apprehension there,
So he with horse and saddle to the mountains did repair.

Then Brennan being an outlaw upon the mountains high,
When cavalry and infantry to take him they did try,
He laughed at them with scorn, until at length, 'tis said,
By a false-hearted young man he basely was betrayed.

In the country of Tipperary, in a place they call Clonmore,
Willie Brennan and his comrade that day did suffer sore.
He lay amongst the fern which was thick upon the field,
And nine deep wounds he did receive before that he did yield.

When Brennan and his comrade found that they were
    betrayed,
They with the mounted cavalry a noble battle made.
He lost his foremost finger, which was shot off by a ball,
So Brennan and his comrade they were taken after all.

So they were taken prisoners, in irons they were bound,
And both conveyed to Clonmel jail, strong walls did them
    surround.
They were tried and there found guilty, the judge made this
    reply,
"For robbing on the king's highway you're both condemned
    to die."

Farewell unto my dear wife and to my children three,
Likewise my aged father, he may shed tears for me,
And to my loving mother, who tore her locks and cried,
Saying, "I wish, my Willie Brennan, in your cradle you had
    died."
    Brennan on the Moor, Brennan on the Moor,
    A brave undaunted robber bold was Brennan on the Moor.

THE WILD COLONIAL BOY

There was a noted hero, Jack Dolan was his name;
Brought up by honest parents, he was reared near Castlemain.
He was his father's only pride and his mother's only joy,
And dearly did his parents love their wild Colonial boy.

It was at the early age of sixteen he left his happy home,
And to Australia's sunny lands was most inclined to roam.
He robbed the rich and helped the poor; he stopped George
    McElroy,
Who trembling gave up his gold to the wild Colonial boy.

Then he bade the squire "Good morning" and he told him
    to beware
To never send a poor boy up while acting on the square;
And never part a mother from her only pride and joy,
For fear he might go rambling like this wild Colonial boy.

It was at the age of eighteen years he began his wild career,
With a heart that knows no danger and a spirit that has no
    fear.
He robbed the rich esquires, and their flocks he did destroy;
He was a terror to Australia, this wild Colonial boy.

One day upon the prairie, as Jack he rode along,
Listening to the mockingbirds singing their sweetest song,
Up rose a mount of troopers: Kelly, Davis, Gilroy;
They all rode up to capture him, this wild Colonial boy.

An Australian Robin Hood

"Surrender now, Jack Dolan, for you see there's three to one,
Surrender in the Queen's name, for you're a plundering son."
Jack drew two pistols from his side and held them up on high.
"I'll fight, but not surrender," cried this wild Colonial boy.

Then he fired a shot at Kelly that brought him to the ground,
And in return from Davis he received his fatal wound.
Then a pistol ball pierced the proud heart from the pistol of
    Gilroy,
And that's the way they captured the wild Colonial boy.

ELEGY ON THE DEATH OF A MAD DOG

Good people all, of every sort,
   Give ear unto my song;
And if you find it wondrous short,
   It cannot hold you long.

In Islington there was a man
   Of whom the world might say,
That still a godly race he ran—
   Whene'er he went to pray.

A kind and gentle heart he had,
   To comfort friends and foes:
The naked every day he clad—
   When he put on his clothes.

And in that town a dog was found,
   As many dogs there be,
Both mongrel, puppy, whelp, and hound,
   And curs of low degree.

This dog and man at first were friends;
   But when a pique began,
The dog, to gain his private ends.
   Went mad, and bit the man.

Around from all the neighboring streets
   The wondering neighbors ran,
And swore the dog had lost his wits,
   To bite so good a man!

The wound it seemed both sore and sad
    To every Christian eye:
And while they swore the dog was mad,
    They swore the man would die.

But soon a wonder came to light,
    That showed the rogues they lied:—
The man recovered of the bite,
    The dog it was that died!

OLIVER GOLDSMITH

from THE MIKADO

NANKI POO: A wandering minstrel I—
              A thing of shreds and patches,
              Of ballads, songs and snatches,
          And dreamy lullaby!

          My catalogue is long,
              Through every passion ranging
              And to your humours changing
          I tune my supple song!

                  Are you in sentimental mood?
                      I'll sigh with you,
                          Oh, sorrow, sorrow!
                  On maiden's coldness do you brood?
                      I'll do so, too—
                          Oh, sorrow, sorrow!
                  I'll charm your willing ears
                  With songs of lovers' fears,
                  While sympathetic tears
                      My cheeks bedew—
                          Oh, sorrow, sorrow!

          But if patriotic sentiment is wanted,
              I've patriotic ballads cut and dried;
          For where'er our country's banner may be
                  planted,
              All other local banners are defied!
          Our warriors, in serried ranks assembled,
              Never quail—or they conceal it if they do—
          And I shouldn't be surprised if nations trembled
              Before the mighty troops of Titipu!

CHORUS: We shouldn't be surprised, etc.

NANKI POO: And if you call for a song of the sea,
We'll heave the capstan round,
With a yeo heave ho, for the wind is free,
Her anchor's a-trip and her helm's a-lee,
Hurrah for the homeward bound!

CHORUS: Yeo-ho—heave ho—
Hurrah for the homeward bound!

NANKI POO: To lay aloft in a howling breeze
May tickle a landsman's taste,
But the happiest hour a sailor sees
Is when he's down
At an inland town,
With his Nancy on his knees, yeo ho!
And his arm around her waist!

CHORUS: Then man the capstan—off we go,
As the fiddler swings us round,
With a yeo heave ho,
And a rumbelow,
Hurrah for the homeward bound!

NANKI POO: A wandering minstrel I, etc.

W. S. GILBERT

THE MARKET

A man said to me at the fair
—If you've got a poet's tongue
Tumble up and chant the air
That the Stars of Morning sung:

—I'll pay you, if you sing it nice,
A penny-piece.—I answered flat,
—Sixpence is the proper price
For a ballad such as that.—

But he stared and wagged his head,
Growling as he passed along
—Sixpence! Why, I'd see you dead
Before I pay that for a song.—

I saw him buy three pints of stout
With the sixpence—dirty lout!

JAMES STEPHENS

JOHN BARLEYCORN

There was three kings into the east,
   Three kings both great and high,
And they hae sworn a solemn oath
   John Barleycorn should die.

They took a plough and plough'd him down,
   Put clods upon his head,
And they hae sworn a solemn oath
   John Barleycorn was dead.

But the cheerful Spring came kindly on,
   And show'rs began to fall;
John Barleycorn got up again,
   And sore surpris'd them all.

The sultry suns of Summer came,
   And he grew thick and strong:
His head weel arm'd wi' pointed spears,
   That no one should him wrong.

The sober Autumn enter'd mild,
   When he grew wan and pale;
His bending joints and drooping head
   Show'd he began to fail.

His colour sicken'd more and more,
   He faded into age;
And then his enemies began
   To show their deadly rage.

John Barleycorn is a personification of barley, the grain
from which Scotch whiskey is made.

They've taen a weapon long and sharp,
    And cut him by the knee;
Then ty'd him fast upon a cart,
    Like a rogue for forgerie.

They laid him down upon his back,
    And cudgell'd him full sore.
They hung him up before the storm,
    And turn'd him o'er and o'er.

They fillèd up a darksome pit
    With water to the brim,
They heaved in John Barleycorn—
    There, let him sink or swim!

They laid him out upon the floor,
    To work him farther woe;
And still, as signs of life appear'd,
    They toss'd him to and fro.

They wasted o'er a scorching flame
    The marrow of his bones;
But a miller us'd him worst of all,
    For he crushed him between two stones.

And they hae taen his very heart's blood,
    And drank it round and round;
And still the more and more they drank,
    Their joy did more abound.

John Barleycorn was a hero bold,
    Of noble enterprise;
For if you do but taste his blood,
    'T will make your courage rise.

'T will make a man forget his woe;
  'T will heighten all his joy:
'T will make the widow's heart to sing,
  Tho' the tear were in her eye.

Then let us toast John Barleycorn,
  Each man a glass in hand;
And may his great posterity
  Ne'er fail in old Scotland!

ROBERT BURNS

THE VICAR OF BRAY

In good King Charles's golden days,
    When loyalty no harm meant,
A zealous high-churchman was I,
    And so I got preferment.
To teach my flock I never missed:
    Kings were by God appointed,
And lost are those that dare resist
    Or touch the Lord's anointed.
      And this is law that I'll maintain
        Until my dying day, sir,
      That whatsoever king shall reign,
        Still I'll be the Vicar of Bray, sir.

When royal James possessed the crown
    And popery grew in fashion,
The penal laws I hooted down,
    And read the Declaration;
The Church of Rome I found would fit
    Full well my constitution;
And I had been a Jesuit
    But for the Revolution.

When William was our king declared
    To ease the nation's grievance,
With this new wind about I steered,
    And swore to him allegiance;
Old principles I did revoke,
    Set conscience at a distance;
Passive obedience was a joke,
    A jest was non-resistance.

When royal Anne became our queen,
    The Church of England's glory,
Another face of things was seen,
    And I became a Tory;
Occasional conformists base,
    I blamed their moderation,
And thought the Church in danger was,
    By such prevarication.

When George in pudding-time came o'er,
    And moderate men looked big, sir,
My principles I changed once more,
    And so became a Whig, sir;
And thus preferment I procured
    From our new Faith's defender,
And almost every day abjured
    The Pope and the Pretender.

The illustrious house of Hanover,
    And Protestant succession,
To these I do allegiance swear—
    While they can keep possession:
For in my faith and loyalty
    I nevermore will falter,
And George my lawful king shall be—
    Until the times do alter.
      And this is law that I'll maintain
        Until my dying day, sir,
      That whatsoever king shall reign,
        Still I'll be the Vicar of Bray, sir.

THE WEARIN' O' THE GREEN

Oh, Paddy dear! and did ye hear the news that's goin' round?
The shamrock is forbid by law to grow on Irish ground!
No more St. Patrick's day we'll keep; his colour can't be seen.
For there's a cruel law ag'in' the Wearin' o' the Green!

I met with Napper Tandy, and he took me by the hand,
And he said, "How's poor ould Ireland, and how does she
    stand?"
She's the most distressful country that ever yet was seen,
For they're hanging men and women there for the Wearin' o'
    the Green.

An' if the colour we must wear is England's cruel red,
Let it remind us of the blood that Ireland has shed;
Then pull the shamrock from your hat, and throw it on the
    sod,
An' never fear, 'twill take root there, though under foot 'tis
    trod.

When law can stop the blades of grass from growin' as they
    grow,
An' when the leaves in summer time their colour dare not
    show,
Then I will change the colour, too, I wear in my caubeen;
But till that day, plaise God, I'll stick to the Wearin' o' the
    Green.

This broadside ballad has survived for over a hundred years as an expression of Irish patriotism.

YANKEE DOODLE

Fath'r and I went down to camp,
    Along with Captain Goodin;
And there we saw the men and boys
    As thick as hasty puddin'.

And there we saw a thousand men,
    As rich as Squire David;
And what they wasted ev'ry day,
    I wish it could be savèd.

And there was Captain Washington
    Upon a slapping stallion,
A giving orders to his men;
    I guess there was a million.

I saw a little barrel, too,
    The head was made of leather;
They knocked upon't with little sticks
    And called the folks together.

And there I saw a swamping gun,
    Big as a log of maple,
Upon a mighty little cart,
    A load for father's cattle.

And every time they shoot it off
    It takes a horn of powder,
And makes a noise like father's gun,
    Only a nation louder.

Dr. Schuckburg was a British army physician. The song was sung derisively
by British soldiers during the Revolution and defiantly taken up by the
Americans.

It scared me so I hooked it off,
　　Nor stopped, as I remember,
Nor turned about till I got home
　　Locked up in Mother's chamber.

Chorus:
Yankee Doodle keep it up,
　　Yankee Doodle dandy,
Mind the music and the step,
　　And with the girls be handy.

DR. RICHARD SCHUCKBURG

THE MOUSE'S COURTING SONG

There was a little mouse who lived on a hill, hm-hm,
There was a little mouse who lived on a hill,
He was rough and tough like Buffalo Bill, hm-hm.

One day he decided to take a ride, hm-hm,
One day he decided to take a ride
With two six-shooters by his side, hm-hm.

Then Mickey rode till he came to a house,
And in this house was Minnie Mouse.

He strutted right up to the kitchen door,
And bowed and scraped his head on the floor.

O Minnie, Minnie, will you marry me?
Away down yonder in the orchard tree!

Without my Uncle Rat's consent,
I would not marry the Pres-eye-dent!

Her Uncle Rat gave his consent,
The Weasel wrote the publishment.

Oh, what you gonna have for the wedding feast?
Black-eyed peas and hogshead cheese.

The first one came was Uncle Rat,
Head as long as a baseball bat.

Second one came was Mr. Snake,
He wrapped himself 'round the marble cake.

This was sung in the Depression by children in the streets of Pittsburgh.

The next one came was a little moth,
To spread on the tablecloth.

The next one came was a big black bug,
Carrying 'round a little brown jug.

The next one came was a bumblebee,
With a broken wing and a crooked knee.

The next one came was a nimble flea,
Saying Minnie, Minnie Mouse, will you dance with me?

The next one came was Mr. Cow,
He wanted to dance but he didn't know how.

Last one came was Mr. Cat,
He ruffled and tuffled and ate Uncle Rat.

And that was the end of the wedding feast,
Black-eyed peas and hogshead cheese.

BROTHER, CAN YOU SPARE A DIME?

They used to tell me I was building a dream
And so I followed the mob.
When there was earth to plough or guns to bear
I was always there—right on the job.
They used to tell me I was building a dream
With peace and glory ahead,
Why should I be standing in line just waiting for bread?
Once I built a railroad, made it run,
Made it race against time.
Once I built a railroad, Now it's done—
Brother, can you spare a dime?
Once I built a tower, to the sun—
Brick and rivet and lime,
Once I built a tower, Now it's done,
Brother, can you spare a dime?
Once in khaki suits, Gee, we looked swell,
Full of that Yankee-Doodle-de-dum.
Half a million boots went sloggin' thru Hell,
I was the kid with the drum.
Say, don't you remember, they called me Al
It was Al all the time.
Say, don't you remember I'm your Pal!
Buddy, can you spare a dime?

E. Y. HARBURG

ॐ *144*

CANADIAN BOAT-SONG

Listen to me, as when ye heard our father
    Sing long ago the song of other shores—
Listen to me, and then in chorus gather
    All your deep voices, as ye pull your oars:

Chorus:
    Fair these broad meads—these hoary woods are grand;
        But we are exiles from our fathers' land.

From the lone shieling of the misty island
    Mountains divide us, and the waste of seas—
Yet still the blood is strong, the heart is Highland,
    And we in dreams behold the Hebrides.

Chorus

We ne'er shall tread the fancy-haunted valley,
    Where 'tween the dark hills creeps the small clear stream,
In arms around the patriarch banner rally,
    Nor see the moon on royal tombstones gleam.

Chorus

When the bold kindred, in the time long vanish'd,
    Conquer'd the soil and fortified the keep—
No seer foretold the children would be banish'd,
    That a degenerate lord might boast his sheep.

Chorus

During the late eighteenth and early nineteenth centuries when many acres of common land were enclosed, i.e. fenced in, hundreds of English and Scottish farmers lost their livelihood. Many of the Scots emigrated to Canada, as this moving ballad relates.

Come foreign rage—let Discord burst in slaughter!
   O then for clansmen true and stern claymore—
The hearts that would have given their blood like water,
   Beat heavily beyond the Atlantic roar.

Chorus

Credited to JOHN GALT, and also to
JOHN WILSON ("Christopher North")

THE STREETS OF LAREDO

O early one morning I walked out like Agag,
Early one morning to walk through the fire
Dodging the pythons that leaked on the pavements
With tinkle of glasses and tangle of wire;

When grimed to the eyebrows I met an old fireman
Who looked at me wryly and thus did he say:
"The streets of Laredo are closed to all traffic,
We won't never master this joker to-day.

"O hold the branch tightly and wield the axe brightly,
The bank is in powder, the banker's in hell,
But loot is still free on the streets of Laredo
And when we drive home we drive home on the bell."

Then out from a doorway there sidled a cockney,
A rocking-chair rocking on top of his head:
"O fifty-five years I been feathering my love-nest
And look at it now—why, you'd sooner be dead."

At which there arose from a wound in the asphalt,
His big wig a-smoulder, Sir Christopher Wren
Saying: "Let them make hay of the streets of Laredo;
When your ground-rents expire I will build them again."

Then twangling their bibles with wrath in their nostrils
From Bonehill Fields came Bunyan and Blake:
"Laredo the golden is fallen, is fallen;
Your flame shall not quench nor your thirst shall not slake."

Based on the traditional cowboy ballad on page 192

ॐ *147*

"I come to Laredo to find me asylum,"
Says Tom Dick and Harry the Wandering Jew;
"They tell me report at the first police station
But the station is pancaked—so what can I do?"

Thus eavesdropping sadly I strolled through Laredo
Perplexed by the dicta misfortunes inspire
Till one low last whisper inveigled my earhole—
The voice of the Angel, the voice of the fire:

O late, very late, have I come to Laredo
A whimsical bride in my new scarlet dress
But at last I took pity on those who were waiting
To see my regalia and feel my caress.

Now ring the bells gaily and play the hose daily,
Put splints on your legs, put a gag on your breath;
O you streets of Laredo, you streets of Laredo,
Lay down the red carpet—My dowry is death.

LOUIS MAC NEICE

*"What are the bugles
    blowin' for?"*

                WAR

O WHAT IS THAT SOUND

O what is that sound which so thrills the ear
   Down in the valley drumming, drumming?
Only the scarlet soldiers, dear,
   The soldiers coming.

O what is that light I see flashing so clear
   Over the distance brightly, brightly?
Only the sun on their weapons, dear,
   As they step lightly.

O what are they doing with all that gear,
   What are they doing this morning, this morning?
Only their usual manoeuvres, dear,
   Or perhaps a warning.

O why have they left the road down there,
   Why are they suddenly wheeling, wheeling?
Perhaps a change in their orders, dear.
   Why are you kneeling?

O haven't they stopped for the doctor's care,
   Haven't they reined their horses, their horses?
Why, they are none of them wounded, dear,
   None of these forces.

O is it the parson they want, with white hair,
   Is it the parson, is it, is it?
No, they are passing his gateway, dear,
   Without a visit.

O it must be the farmer who lives so near.
  It must be the farmer so cunning, so cunning?
They have passed the farmyard already, dear,
  And now they are running.

O where are you going? Stay with me here!
  Were the vows you swore deceiving, deceiving?
No, I promised to love you, dear,
  But I must be leaving.

O it's broken the lock and splintered the door,
  O it's the gate where they're turning, turning;
Their boots are heavy on the floor
  And their eyes are burning.

W. H. AUDEN

THE SAILOR BOY

He rose at dawn and, fired with hope,
   Shot o'er the seething harbor-bar,
And reach'd the ship and caught the rope,
   And whistled to the morning star.

And while he whistled long and loud
   He heard a fierce mermaiden cry,
"O boy, tho' thou art young and proud,
   I see the place where thou wilt lie.

"The sands and yeasty surges mix
   In caves about the dreary bay,
And on thy ribs the limpet sticks,
   And in thy heart the scrawl shall play."

"Fool," he answer'd, "death is sure
   To those that stay and those that roam,
But I will nevermore endure
   To sit with empty hands at home.

"My mother clings about my neck,
   My sisters crying, 'Stay for shame;'
My father raves of death and wreck,—
   They are all to blame, they are all to blame.

"God help me! save I take my part
   Of danger on the roaring sea,
A devil rises in my heart,
   Far worse than any death to me."

ALFRED, LORD TENNYSON

STORMALONG

Oh, Stormy's dead an' gone to rest.
  To m' way-ay, Storm-a-long!
Of all the sail-ors he was best:
  Aye, aye, aye, Mister Storm-a-long!

For fifty year he sailed th' seas.
  To m' way-ay, Storm-a-long
In win-ter storm an' sum-mer breeze.
  Aye, aye, aye, Mister Storm-a-long!

An' now old Stormy's day is done.
  To m' way-ay, Storm-a-long!
We marked th' place whe-ere he is gone.
  Aye, aye, aye, Mister Storm-a-long!

He slipped his cable off Cape Horn.
  To m' way-ay, Storm-a-long!
Far from th' place where he was born.
  Aye, aye, aye, Mister Storm-a-long!

I wish I was old Stormy's son.
  To m' way-ay, Storm-a-long!
I'd build a ship of a thousand ton.
  Aye, aye, aye, Mister Storm-a-long!

I'd load her with New England rum.
  To m' way-ay, Storm-a-long!
An' give ye all, my bull-ies, some.
  Aye, aye, aye, Mister Storm-a-long!

DANNY DEEVER

"What are the bugles blowin' for?" said Files-on-Parade.
"To turn you out, to turn you out," the Colour-Sergeant said.
"What makes you look so white, so white?" said Files-on-
   Parade.
"I'm dreadin' what I've got to watch," the Colour-Sergeant
   said.
   For they're hangin' Danny Deever, you can hear the
     Dead March play,
   The Regiment's in 'ollow square—they're hangin' him to-
     day;
   They've taken of his buttons off an' cut his stripes away,
   An' they're hangin' Danny Deever in the mornin'.

"What makes the rear-rank breathe so 'ard?" said Files-on-
   Parade.
"It's bitter cold, it's bitter cold," the Colour-Sergeant said.
"What makes that front-rank man fall down?" said Files-on-
   Parade.
"A touch o' sun, a touch o' sun," the Colour-Sergeant said.
   They are hangin' Danny Deever, they are marchin' of
     'im round,
   They 'ave 'alted Danny Deever by 'is coffin on the ground;
   An' 'e'll swing in 'arf a minute for a sneakin' shootin'
     hound—
   O they're hangin' Danny Deever in the mornin'!

" 'Is cot was right-and cot to mine," said Files-on-Parade.
"'E's sleepin' out an' far to-night," the Colour-Sergeant said.
"I've drunk 'is beer a score o' times," said Files-on-Parade.
"'E's drinkin' bitter beer alone," the Colour-Sergeant said.
  They are hangin' Danny Deever, you must mark 'im to
    is' place,
  For 'e shot a comrade sleepin'—you must look 'im in the
    face;
  Nine 'undred of 'is county an' the Regiment's disgrace,
  While they're hangin' Danny Deever in the mornin'.

"What's that so black agin the sun?" said Files-on-Parade.
"It's Danny fightin' 'ard for life," the Colour-Sergeant said.
"What's that that whimpers over'ead?" said Files-on-Parade.
"It's Danny's soul that's passin' now," the Colour-Sergeant
    said.
  For they're done with Danny Deever, you can 'ear the
    quickstep play,
  The Regiment's in column, an' they're marchin' us away;
  Ho! the young recruits are shakin', an' they'll want their
    beer to-day,
  After hangin' Danny Deever in the mornin'!

RUDYARD KIPLING

from *OTHELLO*

IAGO. [Sings] "And let me the canakin clink, clink;
           And let me the canakin clink.
              A soldier's a man;
              O, man's life's but a span;
           Why, then, let a soldier drink."

Some wine, boys!
CASSIO. 'Fore God, an excellent song.
IAGO. I learn'd it in England, where, indeed, they are most potent in potting; your Dane, your German, and your swag-belli'd Hollander—Drink, ho—are nothing to your English.

.   .   .   .   .

IAGO. O sweet England!
  "King Stephen was a worthy peer,
    His breeches cost him but a crown;
  He held them sixpence all too dear,
    With that he'd call'd the tailor lown.

  "He was a wight of high renown,
    And thou art but of low degree.
  'Tis pride that pulls the country down;
    Then take thy auld cloak about thee."

WILLIAM SHAKESPEARE

IT WAS A' FOR OUR RIGHTFU' KING

It was a' for our rightfu' king
   We left fair Scotland's strand;
It was a' for our rightfu' king,
   We e'er saw Irish land, my dear,
     We e'er saw Irish land.

Now a' is done that men can do,
   And a' is done in vain:
My Love and Native Land fareweel,
   For I maun cross the main, my dear,
     For I maun cross the main.

He turn'd him right and round about,
   Upon the Irish shore,
And gae his bridle reins a shake,
   With, adieu for evermore, my dear,
     With, adieu for evermore!

The soger frae the wars returns,
   The sailor frae the main,
But I hae parted frae my Love,
   Never to meet again, my dear,
     Never to meet again.

When day is gane, and night is come,
   And a' folk bound to sleep;
I think on him that's far awa,
   The lee-lang night, & weep, my dear,
     The lee-lang night & weep.

ROBERT BURNS

THE SONS OF LIBERTY

O fare you well, sweet Ireland, whom I shall see no more,
My heart is almost bleeding to leave this native shore.
The king he has commanded that we shall sail away
To fight the boys of liberty in North Amerikee.

It was early in next morning, just at the break of day,
We hoisted British colours and anchored in Yorks Bay.
The sails a-being a-lassered they spread abroad to dry.
The Irish heroes landing, but the Lord knows who must die.

The French, the Dutch, the Spaniard, they proved so cruelly
To use our Irish heroes for such barbarity.
They sent on their grape-shot which cut our men aways,
With the sword they showed no quarters in North Amerikee.

Through fields of blood we waded where the cannons loudly
    roar,
And a many a gallant soldier a-bleeding in his gore,
And it's many a gallant commander it's on the field did lay
That was both killed and wounded by the Sons of Liberty.

Your hearts would have melted with pity to have seen the
    soldiers' wives
A hunting for their dead husbands and the melancholy cries,
And the children crying: Mother, we surely rue the day
When we came for to lose our father dear in the North of
    Amerikee.

Here's an end to my ditty, my song is at an end,
Here's a health to General Washington and all of his bold
    men.
God help a man protect him that is by land or sea,
For he had boys who feared no noise and Sons of Liberty.

FAREWELL TO KINGSBRIDGE

On the ninth of November by the dawning of the day
Ere we sailed for New York we did lie in the bay.
O'er the fair fields of Kingsbridge the mist it lay grey,
We were bound against the rebels of North America.

O so sad was the parting 'twixt soldiers and wives
For they knew not if all would return with their lives.
O the women they wept and they cursed the day
That we sailed 'gainst the rebels in North America.

The babes held up their arms with the saddest of cries
And the tears trickled down from their innocent eyes
That their red-coated daddies must hasten away
For to fight with the rebels in North America.

Now God save King George, I will finish my strain.
May his subjects all loyal his honour maintain.
God prosper our voyage and arms across the sea
And pull down the proud rebels in North America.

Kingsbridge is a town in Devonshire in the south of England. It is also
the name of a section of New York City where on July 2, 1781, British
troops repulsed General Washington's attack.

THE RICH LADY OVER THE SEA

There was a rich lady lived over the sea,
And she was an island queen;
Her daughter lived off in the new country,
   With an ocean of water between,
   With an ocean of water between.

The old lady's pockets were fillèd with gold,
   Yet never contented was she;
So she ordered her daughter to pay her a tax
   Of thruppence a pound on the tea,
   Of thruppence a pound on the tea.

"O mother, dear mother," the daughter replied,
   "I'll not do the thing that you ask;
I'm willing to pay a fair price on the tea,
   But never the thruppeny tax,
   But never the thruppeny tax."

"You shall!" cried the mother, and reddened with rage,
   "For you're my own daughter, you see;
And it's only proper that daughter should pay
   Her mother a tax on the tea,
   Her mother a tax on the tea."

She ordered her servant to be called up
   To wrap up a package of tea;
And eager for threepence a pound, she put in
   Enough for a large family,
   Enough for a large family.

She ordered her servant to bring home the tax,
    Declaring her child must obey,
Or, old as she was, and woman most grown,
    She'd half whip her life away,
    She'd half whip her life away.

The tea was conveyed to her daughter's own door,
    All down by the oceanside;
But the bouncing girl poured out every pound
    On the dark and boiling tide,
    On the dark and boiling tide.

And then she called out to the island queen,
    "O mother, dear mother," called she,
"Your tea you may have when 'tis stepped enough,
    But never a tax from me,
    But never a tax from me."

SANTY ANA

Oh, San-ty Ana won th' day.
Hoo-ray, San-ty A-ana!
Oh, San-ty Ana won th' day,
Along th' plains of Mexico!

An' Gen'ral Taylor ran a-way.
Hoo-ray, San-ty A-ana!
He ran away at Mo-on-te-ray.
Along th' plains of Mexico!

Oh, San-ty Ana fought fo-or fame.
Hoo-ray, San-ty A-ana!
Oh, San-ty Ana ma-ade his name.
Along th' plains of Mexico!

Oh, San-ty Ana's dead an' gone.
Hoo-ray, San-ty A-ana! .
When all th' fight-ing he had done.
Along th' plains of Mexico!

We buried him with a gold-en spade.
Hoo-ray, San-ty A-ana!
An' marked th' place where he was laid.
Along th' plains of Mexico!

Don't try to learn history from ballads. Santa Anna, the Mexican general, was in fact defeated by Zachary Taylor in the Mexican-American War.

THE BATTLE OF SHILOH

All you Southerners now draw near,
Unto my story approach you here.
Each loyal Southerner's heart to cheer
With the victory gained at Shiloh.

O it was on April the sixteenth day,
In spite of a long and muddy way,
We landed safe at Corinth Bay
All on our route to Shiloh.

That night we lay on the cold ground,
No tents nor shelters could we find;
And in the rain we almost drowned
All on our way to Shiloh.

Next morning a burning sun did rise
Beneath the eastern cloudless sky,
And General Beauregard replied:
Prepare to march to Shiloh.

And when our Shiloh hove in view,
It would the bravest hearts subdue
To see the Yankee melody crew
That held the works at Shiloh.

For they were strongly fortified
With batteries on the river-side.
Our generals viewed the plains and cried:
We'll get hot work at Shiloh.

The Battle of Shiloh in April of 1862 was one of the great battles of the
Civil War, but there was no clear-cut victory for either side.

And when those batteries strove to gain,
The balls fell around us thick as rain,
And many a hero there was slain,
Upon the plains of Shiloh.

The thirty-third and the Zouaves,
They charged the batteries and gave three cheers,
And General Beauregard rang the airs
With Southern steel at Shiloh.

Their guns and knapsacks they threw down,
They ran like hares before the hounds.
The Yankee Dutch could not withstand
The Southern charge at Shiloh.

Now many a pretty maid did mourn
A lover who'll no more return;
The cruel war has from her torn;
His body lies at Shiloh.

ROLL, ALABAMA, ROLL

When the *Alabama*'s keel was laid,
 Roll, *Alabama*, roll;
It was laid in the yard of Jonathan Laird,
 O, roll, *Alabama*, roll.

It was laid in the yard of Jonathan Laird,
 Roll, *Alabama*, roll;
It was laid in the town of Birkenhead,
 O, roll, *Albama*, roll.

Down the Mersey ways she rolled then,
 Roll, *Alabama*, roll;
Liverpool fitted her with guns and men,
 O, roll, *Alabama* roll.

From the Western Isles she sailed forth,
 Roll, *Alabama*, roll;
To destroy the commerce of the North,
 O, roll, *Alabama*, roll.

To Cherbourg port she sailed one day,
 Roll, *Alabama*, roll;
To take her count of prize monnay,
 O, roll, *Alabama*, roll.

Many a sailor lad he saw his doom,
 Roll, *Alabama*, roll;
When the *Kearsarge* hove in view,
 O, roll, *Alabama*, roll.

The *Alabama*, a Confederate ship of Civil War days, successfully ran the Union blockade until she was sunk by the *Kearsarge*.

A ball from the forward pivot that day,
 Roll, *Alabama*, roll;
Shot the *Alabama's* stern away,
 O, roll, *Alabama*, roll.

Off the three mile limit in '64,
 Roll, *Alabama*, roll;
The *Alabama* sank to the ocean floor,
 O, roll, *Alabama*, roll.

HOW DO YOU DO, ALABAMA!

Oh, I'm goin' to sing a song, and I won't detain you long,
   And I think you'll find the subject is a charmer;
It's about a ship of might, that fought for Union's right,
   And whipped the sneaking pirate *Alabama*.

Chorus:

   How do you do, *Alabama?* How is your "pop goes the
      weasel?"
    You has gone to Davy Jones, to rest your weary bones,
   And Semmes[1] has gone to England wid de measles.

It was off de coast of France, where Semmes commenced to
      dance,
   An' de *Kearsarge* began to play de fiddle;
With good old Yankee cheer, we spoilt his running gear,
   And sent our shot and shell right thro' his middle.

Chorus

Oh, Semmes he took his sword, and dropped it overboard,
   'Cause he didn't like to say he lost his armor;
But a sneaking thief came round, called the royal yacht
   Deer Hound,
   And stole the pirate of the *Alabama*.

Chorus

Now I think it's no disgrace for a man to know his place,
   And the Union is the best, I am a thinkin';
And all I've got to say, if I live till 'lection day,
   I'm goin' to vote for "honest Abe-e Lincoln!"

Chorus

FRED. WILSON

[1] Semmes was the captain of the *Alabama*.

SONG OF THE DYING GUNNER A.A.1.

Oh mother my mouth is full of stars
As cartridges in the tray
My blood is a twin-branched scarlet tree
And it runs all runs away.

Oh *Cooks to the Galley* is sounded off
And the lads are down in the mess
But I lie done by the forrard gun
With a bullet in my breast.

Don't send me a parcel at Christmas time
Of socks and nutty and wine
And don't depend on a long weekend
By the Great Western Railway line.

Farewell, Aggie Weston,[1] the Barracks at Guz,[2]
Hang my tiddley suit on the door
I'm sewn up neat in a canvas sheet
And I shan't be home no more.

H.M.S. Glory
CHARLES CAUSLEY

---

[1] "Aggie Weston's" is the familiar term used by sailors to describe the hostels founded in many seaports by Dame Agnes Weston.
[2] "Guz" is Naval slang for Devonport.

WHEN I WAS HOME
LAST CHRISTMAS . . .

When I was home last Christmas
I called on your family,
Your aunts and your mother, your sister;
They were kind as ever to me.

They told me how well I was looking
And clearly admired my wife;
I drank tea, made conversation,
And played with my bread, or knife.

Your aunts seemed greyer; your mother's
Lame unexpecting smile
Wandered from doily to doily;
Your dead face still

Cast me, with parted lips,
Its tight-rope-walker's look. . . .
But who is there now to notice
If I look or do not look

At a photograph at your mother's?
There is no one left to care
For all we said, and did, and thought—
The world we were.

RANDALL JARRELL

It's work all day
  for the sugar in your tay

                    WORK

FOLK TUNE

When Bunyan swung his whopping axe
The forests strummed as one loud lute,
The timber crashed beside his foot
And sprung up stretching in his tracks.

He had an ox, but his was blue.
The flower in his buttonhole
Was brighter than a parasol.
He's gone. Tom Swift has vanished too,

Who worked at none but wit's expense,
Putting dirigibles together
Out in the yard, in the quiet weather,
Whistling behind Tom Sawyer's fence.

Now when the darkness in my street
Nibbles the last and crusty crumbs
Of sound, and all the city numbs
And goes to sleep upon its feet,

I listen hard to hear its dreams:
John Henry is our nightmare friend,
Whose shoulders roll without an end,
Whose veins pump, pump and burst their seams,

Whose sledge is smashing at the rock
And makes the sickly city toss
And half awake in sighs of loss
Until the screaming of the clock.

John Henry's hammer and his will
Are here and ringing out our wrong,
I hear him driving all night long
To beat the leisured snarling drill.

RICHARD WILBUR

ह✤ *173*

JOHN HENRY

John Henry was a lil baby,
Sittin' on his mama's knee,
Said: "De Big Bend Tunnel on de C. & O. road
Gonna cause de death of me,
Lawd, lawd, gonna cause de death of me."

Cap'n says to John Henry,
"Gonna bring me a steam drill 'round,
Gonna take dat steam drill out on de job,
Gonna whop dat steel on down,
Lawd, Lawd, gonna whop dat steel on down."

John Henry tol' his cap'n,
Lightnin' was in his eye:
"Cap'n, bet yo las' red cent on me,
Fo' I'll beat it to de bottom or I'll die,
Lawd, Lawd, I'll beat it to de bottom or I'll die."

Sun shine hot an' burnin',
Wer'n't no breeze a-tall,
Sweat ran down like water down a hill,
Dat day John Henry let his hammer fall,
Lawd, Lawd, dat day John Henry let his hammer fall.

John Henry went to de tunnel,
An' dey put him in de lead to drive,
De rock so tall an' John Henry so small,
Dat he lied down his hammer an' he cried,
Lawd, Lawd, dat he lied down his hammer an' he cried.

John Henry is a mythical Black hero of railroad-building days. There are
many versions of this ballad.

John Henry started on de right hand,
De steam drill started on de lef'—
"Before I'd let dis steam drill beat me down,
I'd hammer my fool self to death,
Lawd, Lawd, I'd hammer my fool self to death."

White man tol' John Henry,
"Driver cuss yo' soul,
You might beat dis steam an' drill of mine,
When de rocks in dis mountain turn to gol',
Lawd, Lawd, when de rocks in dis mountain turn to gol'."

John Henry said to his shaker,
"Shaker, why don' you sing?
I'm throwin' twelve poun's from my hips on down,
Jes' listen to de col' steel ring,
Lawd, Lawd, jes' listen to de col' steel ring."

Oh, de captain said to John Henry,
"I b'lieve this mountain's sinkin' in."
John Henry said to his captain, oh my!
"Ain' nothin' but my hammer suckin' win',
Lawd, Lawd, ain' nothin' but my hammer suckin' win'."

John Henry tol' his shaker,
"Shaker, you better pray,
For, if I miss dis six-foot steel,
Tomorrow'll be yo' buryin' day,
Lawd, Lawd, tomorrow'll be yo' buryin' day."

John Henry tol' his captain,
"Look yonder what I see—
Yo' drill's done broke an' yo' hole's done choke,
An' you cain' drive steel like me,
Lawd, Lawd, an' you cain' drive steel like me."

De man dat invented de steam drill,
Thought he was mighty fine.
John Henry drove his fifteen feet,
An' de steam drill only made nine,
Lawd, Lawd, an' de steam drill only made mine.

De hammer dat John Henry swung,
It weighed over nine pound;
He broke a rib in his lef-han' side,
An' his intrels fell on de groun',
Lawd, Lawd, an' his intrels fell on de groun'.

All de women's in de Wes',
When dey heared of John Henry's death,
Stood in de rain, flagged de eas'-boun' train,
Goin' where John Henry fell dead,
Lawd, Lawd, going' where John Henry fell dead.

John Henry's lil mother,
She was all dressed in red,
She jumped in bed, covered up her head,
Said she didn't know her son was dead,
Lawd, Lawd, didn't know her son was dead.

Dey took John Henry to de graveyard,
An' dey buried him in de san',
An' every locomotive come roarin' by,
Says, "Dere lays a steel-drivin' man,
Lawd, Lawd, dere lays a steel-drivin' man."

CASEY JONES

Come, all you rounders, if you want to hear
A story 'bout a brave engineer.
Casey Jones was the rounder's name.
On a six eight wheeler, boys, he won his fame.

The caller called Casey at a half past four,
Kissed his wife at the station door,
Mounted to the cabin with his orders in his hand,
And he took his farewell trip to that Promised Land:

Chorus:
    Casey Jones, mounted to the cabin,
    Casey Jones, with his orders in his hand,
    Casey Jones, mounted to the cabin,
    And he took his farewell trip to the Promised Land.

Put in your water and shovel your coal,
Put your head out the window, watch them drivers roll.
I'll run her till she leaves the rail
'Cause I'm eight hours late with that Western mail.

He looked at his watch and his watch was slow,
He looked at the water and the water was low.
He turned to the fireman and then he said,
"We're goin' to reach Frisco but we'll all be dead."

Chorus:
    Casey Jones, goin' to reach Frisco,
    Casey Jones, but we'll be all dead,
    Casey Jones, goin' to reach Frisco,
    We're goin' to reach Frisco, but we'll all be dead.

Casey pulled up that Reno hill,
He tooted for the crossing with an awful shrill.
The switchman knew by the engine's moan
That the man at the throttle was Casey Jones.

He pulled up within two miles of the place,
Number Four stared him right in the face.
He turned to the fireman, said, "Boy, you better jump
'Cause there's two locomotives that's a-goin' to bump."

Chorus:
 Casey Jones, two locomotives,
 Casey Jones, that's a-goin' to bump,
 Casey Jones, two locomotives,
 There's two locomotives that's a-goin' to bump.

Casey said just before he died,
"There's two more roads that I'd like to ride."
The fireman said, "What could that be?
The Southern Pacific and the Santa Fe?"

Mrs. Jones sat on her bed a-sighin',
Just received a message that Casey was dyin'.
Said, "Go to bed, children, and hush your cryin'
'Cause you got another papa on the Salt Lake Line."

Chorus:
 Mrs. Casey Jones, got another papa,
 Mrs. Casey Jones, on that Salt Lake Line,
 Mrs. Casey Jones, got another papa,
 And you've got another papa on the Salt Lake Line.

T. LAWRENCE SEIBERT

THE GRESFORD DISASTER

You've heard of the Gresford disaster,
 The terrible price that was paid;
Two hundred and forty-two [1] colliers were lost,
 And three men of a rescue brigade.

It occurred in the month of September,
 At three in the morning, that pit
Was racked by a violent explosion,
 In the Dennis where gas lay so thick.

The gas in the Dennis deep section
 Was packed there like snow in a drift,
And many a man had to leave the coal-face
 Before he had worked out his shift.

A fortnight before the explosion,
 To the shotfirer, Tomlinson cried:
"If you fire that shot we'll all be blown to hell,"
 And no-one can say that he lied.

The fireman's reports they are missing,
 The records of forty-two days;
The colliery manager had them destroyed
 To cover his criminal ways.

Down there in the dark they are lying,
 They died for nine shillings a day;
They have worked out their shift and now they must lie
 In the darkness until Judgment Day.

---

[1] Actually 265 miners lost their lives including the three rescue workers.

The Lord Mayor of London's collecting,
    To help both our children and wives;
The owners have sent some white lilies
    To pay for the poor colliers' lives.

Farewell, our dear wives and our children,
    Farewell, our old comrades as well;
Don't send your sons down the dark dreary pit;
    They'll be damned like the sinners in hell.

SEEING THE ELEPHANT

When I left the States for gold
Everything I had I sold:
A stove and bed, a fat old sow,
Sixteen chickens and a cow.

Chorus:
So leave, you miners, leave;
    oh leave, you miners, leave,
Take my advice, kill off your lice,
    or else go up in the mountains,
Oh no, lots of dust,
    I'm going to the city to get on a "bust,"
Oh no, lots of dust,
    I'm going to the city to get on a "bust."

Off I started, Yankee-like,
I soon fell in with a lot from Pike,
The next was, "Damn you, back, wo-haw,"
A right smart chance from Arkansaw.

On the Platte we couldn't agree,
Because I had the di-a-ree,
We there split up, I made a break
With one old mule for the Great Salt Lake.

Being brave, I cut and carved,
On the desert nearly starved,
My old mule laid down and died,
I had no blanket, took his hide.

"Seeing the elephant" was the Forty-niner phrase admitting
the enormity of the bonanza illusion.

The poor coyote stole my meat,
Then I had naught but bread to eat,
It was not long till that gave out,
Then how I cursed the Truckee route.

On I travelled through the pines,
At last I found the northern mines;
I stole a dog, got whipt like hell,
Then away I went to Marysville.

There I filled the town with lice,
And robbed the Chinese of their rice;
The people say, "You've got the itch,
Leave here, you lousy son of a ———."

Because I would not pay my bill,
They kicked me out of Downieville;
I stole a mule and lost the trail,
And fetched up in the Hangtown jail.

Canvas roof and paper walls
Twenty horse-thieves in the stalls,
I did as I had done before,
Coyoted out from 'neath the floor.

Then people threatened hard my life
Because I stole a miner's wife;
They showed me a rope, to give me signs,
Then off I went to the southern mines.

I mined awhile, got lean and lank,
And lastly stole a monte-bank;
Went to the city, got a gambler's name,
And lost my bank at the thimble game.

I fell in love with a California girl,
Her eyes were grey, her hair did curl;
Her nose turned up to get rid of her chin,
Says she, "You're a miner, you can't come in."

When the elephant I had seen,
I'm damned if I thought I was green;
And others say, both night and morn,
They saw him coming around the Horn.

If I should make another raise,
In New York sure I'll spend my days;
I'll be a merchant, buy a saw,
So goodbye, mines and Panama.

I AM GOING TO CALIFORNIA

I am going to California
As sure as I am born
And I wonder if I'd better go
A sailing 'round the Horn.
Or had better go by Panama,
The old and beaten way
And see the towers and castles old
With walls so grim and gay.

I think I'll go the other way;
In Ephraim Jones's letter
He says the Nicaragua route
Than the other two is better.
So I'll take a ship some pleasant day,
And sail across the sea,
To find the monster Elephant,
Wherever he may be.

I wonder how the critter looks
And if he doesn't stand
With hind feet on the waters
And fore feet on the land.
Eph says I'll see him, tusks and all
Before I reach the diggin's
With the long tom lashed upon his back
And all a miner's riggins.

I wonder if the tales they tell
Are anything like true
About the steamship company,
The captain and the crew?
I wonder if the passengers
Must really eat such stuff
As beef like leather, cold burnt rice
And a little half raw duff?

I wonder if the pigs do grow
So lank and long and thin,
They tie a bow knot in their tails
To keep the critters in?
Else through the knot holes they would go
Straight way into the ocean
And make among the finny tribe
A wonderful commotion.

I wonder if the steamer sinks
Or blows us all sky-high,
Upon whose shoulders will the blame
And public censure lie?
It's a mighty ticklish business
I've a sort of half a notion
This living in a floating house
Upon a roaring ocean.

YE ANCIENT YUBA MINER
OF THE DAYS OF '49

To you I'll sing a good old song,
   made by a Quaker pate,
Of an ancient Yuba miner,
   who owned no real estate,
But who when asked where he belonged,
   this son of Uncle Sam,
He scratched his head a moment
    then in accents clear and shrill
    straightway ejaculated "Yuba Dam!"
Did this ancient Yuba Miner,
   of the days of '49.

I'm told that simple was his food,
   he used no forks nor spoons,
And with old flour and coffee sacks
   he patched his pantaloons;
He was saucy, lousy, ragged, lank,
   but happy as a clam,
And when interrogated in relation
    to the location from whence he hailed,
    he invariably replied, "Yuba Dam!"
Did this grizzled Yuba Miner,
   of the days of '49.

Upham left San Francisco in the fall of 1850, and arrived in New York 38
days later. He joined his family in Philadelphia, and never again returned
to the Coast.

On a prospecting tour one day
    he struck it very rich,
'Twas on a little mountain stream,
    fornenst the Yuba ditch.
Said he, "This claim of mine I'll sell,
    my purse the dust will cram,"
But when questioned in relation
    to his antecedents, and from whence he came,
    he articulated, "Yuba Dam!"
Did this lucky miner,
    of the days of '49.

He started down to 'Frisco town,
    this man of no estate,
On muleback first, by water then—
    but never mind the date,
And on his way they questioned him,
    this son of Uncle Sam;
They asked him the initials of his front name,
    the mine from whence he came,
    and then he placed his hand beside
    his mouth and roared out, "Yuba Dam!"
Did this jolly Yuba miner,
    of the days of '49.

SAMUEL C. UPHAM

OH, MY DARLING CLEMENTINE

In a cavern, in a canyon,
Excavating for a mine,
Dwelt a miner, 'Forty-Niner,
And his daughter Clementine.

Chorus:
  Oh, my darling, Oh, my darling,
  Oh, my darling Clementine,
  You are lost and gone forever,
  Dreadful sorry, Clementine,

Chorus

Light she was and like a fairy,
And her shoes were number nine;
Herring boxes, without topses
Sandals were for Clementine.

Chorus

Drove she ducklings to the water,
Every morning just at nine;
Hit her foot against a splinter,
Fell into the foaming brine.

Chorus

Ruby lips above the water,
Blowing bubbles soft and fine;
Alas for me! I was no swimmer,
So I lost my Clementine.

Chorus

In a churchyard, near the canyon,
Where the myrtle doth entwine,
There grow roses and other posies,
Fertilized by Clementine.

Chorus

Then the miner, 'Forty-Niner,
Soon began to peak and pine,
Thought he oughter jine his daughter,
Now he's with his Clementine.

Chorus

In my dreams she still doth haunt me,
Robed in garments soaked in brine,
Though in life I used to hug her,
Now she's dead, I'll draw the line.

Chorus

TARRIER'S SONG

Every morning at seven o'clock,
There's twenty tarriers a-working at the rock;
And the boss comes along and he says, "Kape still,
And come down heavy with the cast iron drill."

Chorus:

    Drill, ye tarriers, drill.
    Drill, ye tarriers, drill.
    It's work all day for the sugar in your tay.
    Down behind the railway,
    And drill, ye tarriers, drill.
    And blast,
    And fire.

Now our foreman was Jean McCann,
By God, he was a blame mean man;
Past week a premature blast went off,
And a mile in the air went big Jim Goff.

Chorus

Next time pay day comes around,
Jim Goff a dollar short was found;
When asked, "What for?" came this reply:
"You're docked for the time you was up in the sky."

Chorus

The boss was a fine man down to the ground,
And he married a lady six feet 'round;
She baked good bread, and she baked it well,
But she baked it hard as the holes of hell.

Chorus

WORKING IN THE MINES

Working in the mines, boys,
Mighty hard to stand;
Lordy, lordy, these old mines
Has killed a many a man.

Buckets on our arms, boys,
Watch them miners go;
Got to reach the hill on time;
Hear the whistle blow!

See that man a-comin',
Time book in his hand;
Super pays him by the month
To rob the workin' man.

Loaded coal all day, boys;
Ding-dong says we eat;
Rice and bull-dog gravy,
But not a bite of meat.

Mine boss at the office
Cutting down our pay;
Hard times at Mossy Bottom,
But here I guess I'll stay.

An Appalachian ballad

AS I WALKED OUT IN THE STREETS OF LAREDO

As I walked out in the streets of Laredo,
As I walked out in Laredo one day,
I spied a poor cowboy wrapped up in white linen,
Wrapped up in white linen and cold as the clay.

"I see by your outfit that you are a cowboy,"
These words he did say as I boldly stepped by.
"Come sit down beside me and hear my sad story;
I was shot in the breast and I know I must die.

"Let sixteen gamblers come handle my coffin,
Let sixteen cowboys come sing me a song,
Take me to the graveyard and lay the sod o'er me,
For I'm a poor cowboy and I know I've done wrong.

"It was once in the saddle I used to go dashing,
It was once in the saddle I used to go gay.
'Twas first to drinking and then to card playing,
Got shot in the breast, I am dying today.

"Get six jolly cowboys to carry my coffin,
Get six pretty girls to carry my pall;
Put bunches of roses all over my coffin,
Put roses to deaden the clods as they fall.

"O beat the drum slowly and play the fife lowly
And play the dead march as you carry me along,
Take me to the green valley and lay the sod o'er me,
For I'm a young cowboy and I know I've done wrong."

We beat the drum slowly and played the fife lowly,
And bitterly wept as we bore him along;
For we all loved our comrade, so brave, young, and handsome,
We all loved our comrade although he'd done wrong.

THE WILD LUMBERJACK

One day I was out walking on the mountain,
  A wood robin was singing. I happened to spy
A handsome young lumberjack on the banks of the river,
  All dressed in white linen, and laid out to die.

Chorus:
  So beat your drum lowly, and play your fife slowly,
    And play the dead march as you carry me along.
  Oh, take me to the mountain, and lay the sod o'er me,
    For I'm a wild lumberjack and I know I've done wrong.

Once out in the forest I used to go slashing;
  Once in the big timbers I used to be gay.
I first took to drinking, and then to card playing,
  Was shot in the breast, and I'm dying today.

Go, someone, write to my gray-haired mother,
  And also to my brothers and my sisters so dear;
But there is another far dearer than mother,
  Who'd bitterly weep if she knew I was here.

Go, someone, and bring me a cup of cold water—
  A cup of spring water, the poor woodsie said;
But ere it had reached him his spirit had vanished—
  Gone to the Giver, the poor fellow was dead.

A woodsman's version of "The Streets of Laredo," sung in the Potter
County (Pennsylvania) logging camps.

THE BROKEN WEDDING RING

A cowboy with his sweetheart stood beneath a starlit sky,
Tomorrow he was leaving for the lonesome prairie wide.

She said, "I'll be your loving bride when you return some
    day."
He handed her a broken ring and to her he did say:

"You'll find upon that ring, sweetheart, my name engraved
    in gold,
And I will keep the other half, which has your name you
    know."

He went away to ride and toil, this cowboy brave and bold,
But long he stayed and while he strayed the maiden's love
    grew cold.

Three years had passed, he did not come, and Nell will wed
    tonight.
Her father said an earl would make her happy home so bright.

The lights were gaily glowing as they stood there side by
    side.
"Let's drink a toast to this young man and to his lovely bride."

Just then there stood within the door a figure tall and slim,
A handsome cowboy was their guest and slowly he walked in.

"I'll drink with you a toast," said he, and quickly in her glass
He dropped his half of wedding ring, then anxiously he
    watched.

She tipped her glass and from her lips a ring fell shining
    bright.
The token she had longed to see lay there beneath the light.

"Tho' years have been between us, dear, love has won our
    last long fight,
It's you, my cowboy sweetheart, and my Jack I'll wed
    tonight."

O, SAY MY JOLLY FELLOW

"O, say my jolly fellow,
  How would you like to go,
And spend a pleasant winter,
  Up in Canaday-I-O?"

"A-goin' up to Canaday"
  Is what the young men say,
"And a-goin' up to Canaday
  Depends upon the pay."

"O, yes, we'll pay good wages,
  We'll pay your passage out,
Providin' you'll sign papers
  That you will stay the route.

"Or if you should get homesick,
  And say to home you'll go,
We could not pay your passage
  Out of Canaday-I-O."

Then we had a pleasant journey
  The route we had to go,
Till we landed at Three Rivers
  Up in Canaday-I-O.

Then Norcross' and Davis' agents,
  They would come prowling round
And say, "My jolly fellows,
  Why don't you all lay down?"

Our food the dogs would laugh at,
  Our beds was on the snow,
And we suffered worse 'an pizen
  In Canaday-I-O.

I have seen a version of this ballad in which
the young men are lured to Michigan I-O.

GOING UP THE RIVER

Going up the river
From Catlettsburg to Pike,
Working on a push boat
For old man Jeffry's Ike.

Working on a push boat
For fifty cents a day;
Buy my girl a brand-new dress
And throw the rest away.

Working on a push boat,
Water's mighty slack;
Taking sorghum 'lasses down,
And bringing sugar back.

Pushing mighty hard, boys,
Sand bar's in the way;
Working like a son-of-a-gun
For mighty scanty pay.

Going down Big Sandy,
With Pete and Lazy Sam;
When I get to Catlettsburg,
I'll buy myself a dram.

Going down the river,
I live on Buffalo;
Lordy, lordy, Cynthie Jane,
Don't I hate to go.

I wish I had a nickel,
I wish I had a dime;
I'd spend it all on Cynthie Jane
And dress her mighty fine.

The weather's mighty hot, boys,
Blisters on my feet;
Working on a push boat
To buy my bread and meat.

Working on a push boat,
Working in the rain;
When I get to Catlettsburg,
Good-bye, Cynthie Jane.

GET UP AND BAR THE DOOR

It fell about the Martinmas time,
    And a gay time it was then,
When our goodwife got puddings to make,
    And she's boild them in the pan.

The wind sae cauld blew south and north,
    And blew into the floor;
Quoth our goodman to our goodwife,
    "Gae out and bar the door."

"My hand is in my hussyfskap,
    Goodman, as ye may see;
An it shoud nae be barrd this hundred year,
    It's no be barrd for me."

They made a paction tween them twa,
    They made it firm and sure,
That the first word whaeer shoud speak,
    Shoud rise and bar the door.

Then by there came two gentlemen,
    At twelve o clock at night,
And they could neither see house nor hall,
    Nor coal nor candle-light.

"Now whether is this a rich man's house,
    Or whether is it a poor?"
But neer a word wad ane o them speak,
    For barring of the door.

And first they ate the white puddings,
    And then they ate the black;
Tho muckle thought the goodwife to hersel,
    Yet neer a word she spake.

Then said the one unto the other,
 "Here, man, tak ye my knife;
Do ye tak aff the auld man's beard,
 And I'll kiss the goodwife."

"But there's nae water in the house,
 And what shall we do than?"
"What ails ye at the pudding-broo,
 That boils into the pan?"

O up then started our goodman,
 An angry man was he:
"Will ye kiss my wife before my een,
 And scad me wi pudding-bree?"

Then up and started our goodwife,
 Gied three skips on the floor:
"Goodman, you've spoken the foremost word,
 Get up and bar the door."

THE WIFE WRAPT IN WETHER'S SKIN

Sweet William he married a wife,
  Gentle Jenny cried rosemaree
To be the sweet comfort of his life.
  As the dew flies over the mulberry tree.

Jenny couldnt in the kitchen to go,
For fear of dirting her white-heeled shoes.

Jenny couldnt wash, and Jenny couldnt bake,
For fear of dirting her white apurn tape.

Jenny couldnt card, and Jenny couldnt spin,
For fear of hurting her gay gold ring.

Sweet William came whistling in from plaow,
Says, "O my dear wife, is my dinner ready naow?"

She called him a dirty paltry whelp:
"If you want any dinner, go get it yourself."

Sweet William went aout unto the sheepfold,
And aout a fat wether [1] he did pull.

And daown on his knees he began for to stick,
And quicklie its skin he thereof did strip.

He took the skin and laid on his wife's back,
And with a good stick went whikety whack.

"I'll tell my father and all my kin
How still a quarrel you've begun."

[1] sheep

A New England version of a Scottish Ballad

"You may tell your father and all your kin
How I have thrashed my fat wether's skin."

Sweet William came whistling in from plaow,
Says, "O my dear wife, is my dinner ready naow?"

She drew her table and spread her board,
And, "Oh my dear husband," was every word.

And naow they live free from all care and strife,
And naow she makes William a very good wife.

"And love is deeper
nor the sea"

LOVE

THE PRETTY PLOUGHBOY

As I was a-walking
    One morning in spring
I heard a pretty ploughboy,
    And so sweetly he did sing;

And as he was a-singing O
    These words I heard him say,
"There's no life like the ploughboy's
    In the sweet month of May."

There's the lark in the morning
    She will rise up from her nest,
And she'll mount the white air
    With the dew all on her breast.

And with the pretty ploughboy O
    She'll whistle and she'll sing
And at night she'll return
    To her nest back again.

SING ME A SONG

Sing me a song of a lad that is gone,
    Say, could that lad be I?
Merry of soul he sailed on a day
    Over the sea to Skye.

Mull was astern, Rum on the port,
    Egg on the starboard bow;
Glory of youth glowed in his soul:
    Where is that glory now?

Sing me a song of a lad that is gone,
    Say, could that lad be I?
Merry of soul he sailed on a day
    Over the sea to Skye.

Give me again all that was there,
    Give me the sun that shone!
Give me the eyes, give me the soul,
    Give me the lad that's gone!

Sing me a song of a lad that is gone,
    Say, could that lad be I?
Merry of soul he sailed on a day
    Over the sea to Skye.

Billow and breeze, islands and seas,
    Mountains of rain and sun,
All that was good, all that was fair,
    All that was me is gone.

ROBERT LOUIS STEVENSON

SONG TO THE NINTH GRADE

The earth grows green; the flowers bloom;
A red bird sings in the lilac tree.
The leaving day comes soon, comes soon;
And the red bird sings so sweetly, O.

You leave with laughter and beating hearts;
The red bird sings so sweetly, O.
The world holds out its hands to you,
And the red bird sings so sweetly, O.

You leave without a backward glance—
The red bird sings so sweetly, O—
To greet the world so fair and new,
And the red bird sings so sweetly, O.

The years will pass, and flowers fade,
And no bird sing in the lilac tree.
Remember then the days of youth,
When the red bird sang so sweetly, O.

PAMELA CRAWFORD HOLAHAN

Mrs. Holahan, a teacher, wrote this ballad as a farewell to one of her classes.

THE MAYERS' SONG

Remember us poor Mayers all,
   And thus we do begin
To lead our lives in righteousness
   Or else we die in sin.

We have been rambling all this night,
   And almost all this day,
And now returned back again
   We have brought you a branch of May.[1]

A branch of May we have brought you,
   And at your door it stands,
It is but a sprout, but it's well budded out
   By the work of our Lord's hands.

The hedges and trees they are so green,
   As green as any leek,
Our heavenly Father he watered them
   With his heavenly dew so sweet.

The heavenly gates are open wide,
   Our paths are beaten plain,
And if a man be not too far gone
   He may return again.

[1] May: the hawthorn

In rural England, well into the nineteenth century, there were festivities
on May day; groups of youngsters went from door to door with bunches
of flowers or branches of hawthorn to celebrate the coming of the May.

The life of man is but a span,
   It flourishes like a flower,
We are here to-day, and gone to-morrow
   And we are dead in an hour.

The moon shines bright and the stars give a light
   A little before it is day,
So God bless you all, both great and small,
   And send you a joyful May.

THE LADY'S FAREWELL

from the 13th century Galician

Awake, my love, who sleep into the dawn!
The birds of all the world cried and are gone.
I go away in joy.

Awake, my love, who sleep so late at dawn!
It was our love the small birds dwelt upon.
I go away in joy.

The birds of all the world spoke of our love,
Of my love and of yours cried out above.
I go away in joy.

The birds of all the world sang loud at day.
It was my love and yours, I heard them say.
I go away in joy.

It was my love and yours that made their song.
You cut the branches where they clung so long.
I go away in joy.

It was my love and yours that made their cry—
You cut the branches where they used to fly.
I go away in joy.

You cut the branches where they used to sing,
And where they came to drink you dried the spring.
    I go away in joy.

You cut the branches where they used to stay,
And dried the waters where they came to play.
    I go away in joy.

—Nuño Fernández Torneol

YVOR WINTERS

from *THE WINTER'S TALE*

When daffodils begin to peer,
   With, heigh! the doxy over the dale,
Why then comes in the sweet o' the year,
   For the red blood reigns in the winter's pale.

The white sheet bleaching on the hedge,
   With hey! the sweet birds, O how they sing:
Doth set my pugging tooth on edge,
   For a quart of ale is a dish for a king.

The lark, that tirra-lyra chants,
   With heigh! with hey! the thrush and the jay:
Are summer songs for me and my aunts,
   While we lie tumbling in the hay.

WILLIAM SHAKESPEARE

THE RIDDLING KNIGHT

There were three sisters fair and bright,
  Jennifer, Gentle and Rosemary,
And they three loved one valiant knight—
  As the dow [1] *flies over the mulberry-tree.*

The eldest sister let him in,
And barr'd the door with a silver pin.

The second sister made his bed,
And placed soft pillows under his head.

The youngest sister that same night
Was resolved for to wed wi' this valiant knight.

"And if you can answer questions three,
O then, fair maid, I'll marry wi' thee.

"O what is louder nor a horn,
Or what is sharper nor a thorn?

"Or what is heavier nor the lead,
Or what is better nor the bread?

"Or what is longer nor the way,
Or what is deeper nor the sea?"—

"O shame is louder nor a horn,
And hunger is sharper nor a thorn.

[1] dove

ॐ 213

"O sin is heavier nor the lead,
The blessing 's better nor the bread.

"O the wind is longer nor the way
And love is deeper nor the sea."

"You have answer'd aright my questions three,
 Jennifer, Gentle and Rosemary;
And now, fair maid, I'll marry wi' thee,
 As the dow flies over the mulberry-tree."

WHITTINGHAM FAIR

Are you going to Whittingham Fair?
  Parsley, sage, rosemary, and thyme;
Remember me to one who lives there,
  For once she was a true love of mine.

Tell her to make me a cambric shirt,
  Parsley, sage, rosemary, and thyme;
Without any seam or needlework,
  For once she was a true love of mine.

Tell her to wash it in yonder well,
  Parsley, sage, rosemary, and thyme;
Where never spring water or rain ever fell,
  For once she was a true love of mine.

Tell her to dry it on yonder thorn,
  Parsley, sage, rosemary, and thyme;
Which never bore blossom since Adam was born,
  For once she was a true love of mine.

Now he has asked me questions three,
  Parsley, sage, rosemary, and thyme;
I hope he will answer as many for me,
  For once he was a true love of mine.

Tell him to find me an acre of land,
  Parsley, sage, rosemary, and thyme,
Betwixt the salt water and the sea-sand,
  For once he was a true love of mine.

Tell him to plough it with a ram's horn,
　Parsley, sage, rosemary, and thyme,
And sow it all over with one pepper corn,
　For once he was a true love of mine.

Tell him to reap it with a sickle of leather,
　Parsley, sage, rosemary, and thyme,
And bind it up with a peacock's feather,
　For once he was a true love of mine.

When he has done and finished his work,
　Parsley, sage, rosemary, and thyme.
O tell him to come and he'll have his shirt,
　For once he was a true love of mine.

JOHNNY'S THE LAD I LOVE

As I roved out on a May morning,
Being in the youthful spring,
I leaned my back close to the garden wall,
To hear the small birds sing.

And to hear two lovers talk, my dear,
To know what they would say,
That I might know a little of her mind
Before I would go away.

"Come sit you down, my heart," he says,
"All on this pleasant green,
It's full three-quarters of a year and more
Since together you and I have been."

"I will not sit on the grass," she said,
"Now nor any other time,
For I hear you're engaged with another maid,
And your heart is no more of mine.

"Oh, I'll not believe what an old man says,
For his days are well nigh done.
Nor will I believe what a young man says,
For he's fair to many a one.

"But I will climb a high, high tree,
And rob a wild bird's nest,
And I'll bring back whatever I do find
To the arms I love the best," she said,
"To the arms I love the best."

GO FROM MY WINDOW

Begone, begone, my Willie, my Billy,
Begone, my love and my dear.
O the wind and the rain have sent him back again
And you cannot have a lodging here.

Begone, begone, my Willie, my Billy,
Begone, my love and my dear.
O the weather it is warm, it will never do thee harm
And thou canst not have a lodging here.

Begone, begone, my Willie, my Billy,
Begone, my love and my dear.
For the wind is in the west and the cuckoo's in his nest
And thou canst not have a lodging here.

Begone, begone, my Willie, thou silly,
Begone, my fool and my fear.
O the devil's in the man that he cannot understan'
That tonight he cannot lodge in here.

To the tune, "My heart's
as gay as a young sunflower"

Oh, who will shoe your pretty little foot,
   And who will glove your hand,
And who will kiss your cherry red lips,
   When I'm gone to the foreign land?

My pappy'll shoe my pretty little foot,
   And my mammy'll glove my hand,
And there's plenty of boys'll kiss my cherry red lips,
   When you're gone to the foreign land.

Oh, who will comb your golden hair
   With the brand new turtle comb,
And who will kiss your satin neck,
   When I'm gone across the foam?

Oh, my sis will comb my golden hair,
   With the dark red turtle comb;
And I'll find them'll kiss my neck,
   Before ever you come home.

The doves fly off to the woods from the cote,
   But at night they all come home;
And my heart will turn like that to you,
   No matter how far I may roam.

Oh, the wild birds fly all day in the woods,
   From tree to tree they roam;
My heart's like the birds that have not cote,
   Wherever they roost is their home.

Oh, the crow is the bird with the blackest wing,
    And it turns to a purple hue;
If ever I loose this love that I hold,
    Let my body waste like the dew.

On top of the church is a bird that sits,
    And he turns with the winds as they blow;
My heart's not ready to hold to a man,
    So why do you plague me so?

My heart's as clear as a pane of glass,
    Your name's carved there in gold;
It'll stay right there till the day I die,
    For all men to behold.

KENNETH REXROTH

MELORA'S SONG

from *John Brown's Body*

Love came by from the riversmoke,
   When the leaves were fresh on the tree,
But I cut my heart on the blackjack oak
   Before they fell on me.

The leaves are green in the early Spring,
   They are brown as linsey now,
I did not ask for a wedding-ring
   From the wind in the bending bough.

Fall lightly, lightly, leaves of the wild,
   Fall lightly on my care,
I am not the first to go with child
   Because of the blowing air.

I am not the first nor yet the last
   To watch a goosefeather sky,
And wonder what will come of the blast
   And the name to call it by.

Snow down, snow down, you whitefeather bird,
   Snow down, you winter storm,
Where the good girls sleep with a gospel word
   To keep their honor warm.

The good girls sleep in their modesty,
   The bad girls sleep in their shame,
But I must sleep in the hollow tree
   Till my child can have a name.

Melora, a Southern girl, has fallen in love with a Yankee soldier
and bears his child in the wilderness.

I will not ask for the wheel and thread
    To spin the labor pain,
Or the scissors hidden under the bed
    To cut the bearing-pain.

I will not ask for the prayer in church
    Or the preacher saying the prayer,
But I will ask the shivering birch
    To hold its arms in the air.

Cold and cold and cold again,
    Cold in the blackjack limb
The winds of the sky for his sponsor-men
    And a bird to christen him.

Now listen to me, you Tennessee corn,
    And listen to my word,
This is the first child ever born
    That was christened by a bird.

He's going to act like a hound let loose
    When he comes from the blackjack tree,
And he's going to walk in proud shoes
    All over Tennessee.

I'll feed him milk out of my own breast
    And call him Whistling Jack.
And his dad'll bring him a partridge nest,
    As soon as his dad comes back.

STEPHEN VINCENT BENÉT

RARE WILLIE DROWNED IN YARROW

Willy's rare, and Willy's fair,
  And Willy's wondrous bony,
And Willy heght to marry me,
  Gin eer he marryd ony.

Yestreen I made my bed fu brade,
  The night I'll make it narrow,
For a' the live-long winter's night
  I lie twin'd of my marrow.

O came you by yon water-side?
  Pu'd you the rose or lilly?
Or came you by yon meadow green?
  Or saw you my sweet Willy?

She sought him east, she sought him west,
  She sought him brade and narrow
Sine in the clifting of a craig
  She found him drownd in Yarrow.

THE LOWLANDS OF HOLLAND

Oh yesterday I was married, last night I went to bed.
Up came a bold sea-captain and stood by my bedside.
Arise, arise, young married man and go along with me
To the Lowlands of Holland to face your enemy.

Holland is a pleasant place which shines as it stands
And there's good accommodation for sailors in that land,
Where sugar there in canes do grow, the tea falls from the
 tree.
I wish to God my love was nigh, although she's far away.

I'll build my love a galliant ship, a ship of noble fame
Where there's four and twenty stout young men to box her
 on the main,
To box her on the main, my boys, most glorious to behold.
May the God above protect my love, he's a jolly sailor bold.

Nor shall a shoe go on my foot nor a comb go through my
 hair,
Nor fire bright nor candle-light shall shine my beauty fair,
Neither will I married be until the day I die
For the raging seas and the stormy winds have parted my
 love and I.

SOLDIER, WON'T YOU MARRY ME?

Soldier, soldier, won't you marry me?
It's O a fife and drum.
How can I marry such a pretty girl as you
When I've got no hat to put on?

Off to the tailor she did go
As hard as she could run,
Brought him back the finest was there.
Now, soldier, put it on.

Soldier, soldier, won't you marry me?
It's O a fife and drum.
How can I marry such a pretty girl as you
When I've got no coat to put on?

Off to the tailor she did go
As hard as she could run,
Brought him back the finest was there.
Now, soldier, put it on.

Soldier, soldier, won't you marry me?
It's O a fife and drum.
How can I marry such a pretty girl as you
When I've got no shoes to put on?

Off to the shoe shop she did go
As hard as she could run,
Brought him back the finest was there.
Now, soldier, put them on.

Soldier, soldier, won't you marry me?
It's O a fife and drum.
How can I marry such a pretty girl as you
And a wife and a baby at home?

&~ 225

ONE MORNING IN MAY
(THE NIGHTINGALE)

One morning, one morning, one morning in May
I spied a fair couple a-making their way.
One was a lady so bright and so fair,
And the other was a soldier, a gay cavalier.

"Oh, where are you going, my pretty fair maid?
Oh, where are you going, sweet lady?" he said.
"I'm going," said she, "to the banks of the stream,
To see the waters gliding, hear the nightingales sing."

They had not been there but an hour or two
Till out of his satchel a fiddle he drew.
He played her a love-song caused the valleys to ring.
"Hark, hark!" says the lady, "hear the nightingales sing!"

"Oh, now," says the soldier, " 'tis time to give o'er."
"Oh, no," says the lady, "just play one tune more;
For I'd rather hear the fiddle, or one tug on the string,
Than to see the water gliding, hear the nightingales sing.

"Oh, now," says the lady, "it's won't you marry me?"
"Oh no," says the soldier, "that never can be!
I've a wife in Low Flanders, with children twice three;
And two and the army's too many for me!

"I'll go home to Flanders and stay there one year.
In place of pure water I'll drink wine and beer.
And if ever I return, 'twill be in the spring
When the waters are gliding and the nightingales sing."

This is a seventeenth century ballad preserved in America through oral
tradition. This version comes from Missouri.

Come all ye fair damsels, take warning from me.
Never place your affections on a green willow tree;
For the leaves they will wither like flowers in the spring
While the waters are a-gliding and the nightingales sing.

Come all ye fair damsels, take warning from me,
Never place your affections on a soldier so free.
For he'll love you and leave you without any ring
To rock your young baby, hear the nightingales sing!

I'M GOING TO GEORGIA

I'm going to Georgia, I'm going to roam,
I'm going to Georgia to make it my home.

I once loved a young man as dear as my life,
And he oft-times did promise to make me his wife.

The promise he fulfilled and he made me his wife,
And you see what I've come to by believing his lies.

Come all ye fair ladies, take warning by me,
Never cast your affections on a green growing tree.

The leaves they may wither, the flowers they may die,
Some young man may fool you as one has fooled I.

THE SEEDS OF LOVE

I sowed the seeds of love,
 And I sowed them in the spring;
I gathered them up in the morning so soon,
 While the small birds so sweetly sing,
 While the small birds so sweetly sing.

My garden was planted well,
 With flowers everywhere,
But I had not the liberty to choose for myself
 Of the flowers that I loved so dear.

The gard'ner was standing by,
 And I asked him to choose for me;
He chose for me the violet, the lily and the pink,
 But those I refused all three.

The violet I did not like,
 Because it bloomed so soon;
The lily and the pink I really overthink,
 So I vowed that I would wait till June.

In June there was a red rose-bud,
 And that is the flower for me.
I oftentimes have plucked that red rose-bud,
 Till I gained the willow tree.

The willow tree will twist,
   And the willow tree will twine;
I oftentimes have wished I were in that young man's arms
   That once had the heart of mine.

Come all you false young men,
   Do not leave me here to complain,
For the grass that has oftentimes been trampled underfoot
   Give it time, it will rise up again.
     Give it time, it will rise up again.

from OTHELLO

DESDEMONA. My mother had a maid call'd Barbara;
She was in love, and he she lov'd prov'd mad
And did forsake her. She had a song of "willow";
An old thing 'twas, but it express'd her fortune,
And she died singing it. That song to-night
Will not go from my mind: I have much to do
But to go hang my head all at one side
And sing it like poor Barbara.
.   .   .   .   .

   "The poor soul sat sighing by a sycamore tree,
      Sing all a green willow;
Her hand on her bosom, her head on her knee,
      Sing willow, willow, willow.
The fresh streams ran by her, and murmur'd her moans;
      Sing willow, willow, willow;
Her salt tears fell from her, and soft'ned the stones;
      Sing willow, willow, willow;"
   Lay by these:—
[Singing.] Sing willow, willow, willow;
.   .   .   .   .

[Singing.]
   "Sing all a green willow must be my garland.
   Let nobody blame him, his scorn I approve,"—
Nay, that's not next.—Hark! who is't that knocks?
Emilia. It is the wind.
Desdemona. [Singing.]
   "I call'd my love false love; but what said he then?
   Sing willow, willow, willow.
   If I court more women, you'll couch with more men."—

WILLIAM SHAKESPEARE

COSSANTE

from the 13th century Galician

Tell me, daughter, my pretty daughter,
Why you waited by the cold water.
            —It was love, alas!

Tell me, daughter, my lovely daughter,
Why you waited by the cold water.
            —It was love, alas!

I waited, mother, by the cold fountain
While the deer came down the mountain.
            —It was love, alas!

I waited by the cold river, mother,
To see the deer, and not for any other.
            —It was love, alas!

You lie, daughter, you lie for your lover,
I never saw deer come down from cover.
            —It was love, alas!

You lie, daughter, for your lover by the fountain,
I never saw deer going up to the mountain.
            —It was love, alas!
                                    —Pero Meogo

                              YVOR WINTERS

from HAMLET

OPHELIA. [*Sings.*]
    "How should I your true love know
      From another one?
    By his cockle hat and staff,
      And his sandal shoon."

QUEEN. Alas, sweet lady, what imports the song?

OPHELIA. Say you? Nay, pray you, mark.
    [*Sings.*] "He is dead and gone, lady,
      He is dead and gone;
        At his head a grass-green turf
        At his heels a stone."

          Enter KING.
QUEEN. Nay, but, Ophelia,—

OPHELIA. Pray you, mark.
[*Sings.*] "White his shroud as the mountain snow,"—

QUEEN. Alas, look here, my lord.

OPHELIA. [*Sings.*]
    "Larded with sweet flowers;
    Which bewept to the grave did not go
      With true-love showers."

KING. How do you, pretty lady?

OPHELLA. Well, God 'ild you! They say the owl was a baker's daughter. Lord, we know what we are, but know not what we may be. God be at your table!

KING. Conceit upon her father.

OPHELIA. Pray you, let's have no words of this,
but when they ask you what it means, say you this:
[*Sings.*] "Tomorrow is Saint Valentine's day
    All in the morning betime,
And I a maid at your window,
    To be your Valentine.

"Then up he rose and donn'd his clothes,
    And dupp'd the chamber door,
Let in the maid, that out a maid
    Never departed more."

KING. Pretty Ophelia!

OPHELIA. Indeed, la, without an oath I'll make an end on't.
   "By gis, and by Saint Charity,
      Alack! and, Fie for shame!
   Young men will do't if they come to't;
      By Cock, they are to blame.

   "Quoth she, 'Before you tumbled me,
      You promis'd me to wed.'
   'So would I ha' done, by yonder sun,
      An thou hadst not come to my bed.' " [1]

WILLIAM SHAKESPEARE

[1] This vulgar St. Valentine's ballad sung by the gentle Ophelia seems to sum up the shock and horror of her madness.

THE APPARITION

My pillow won't tell me
  Where he has gone,
The soft-footed one
  Who passed by, alone.

Who took my heart, whole,
  With a tilt of his eye,
And with it, my soul,
  And it like to die.

I twist, and I turn,
  My breath but a sigh.
Dare I grieve? Dare I mourn?
  He walks by. He walks by.

THEODORE ROETHKE

TRUELOVE

"Father, what is truelove,
That they sing about?"
"It's something, little daughter,
You can do without."

"Mother, what is truelove?
I'm old enough to know."
"If you were, my darling,
I would tell you so."

"Brother, what is truelove?
Be serious with me."
"I will. But it is something
That cannot ever be."

"Sister, what is truelove?—
Oh, dear, why are you crying?"
"Because someone has left me,
And my heart is dying."

MARK VAN DOREN

SHE MOVED THROUGH THE FAIR

My young love said to me, "My brothers won't mind,
And my parents won't slight you for your lack of kind."
Then she stepped away from me, and this she did say
"It will not be long, love, till our wedding day."

She stepped away from me and she moved through the fair,
And fondly I watched her go here and go there,
Then she went her way homeward with one star awake,
As the swan in the evening moves over the lake.

The people were saying no two were ere wed
But one had a sorrow that never was said,
And I smiled as she passed with her goods and her gear,
And that was the last that I saw of my dear.

I dreamt it last night that my young love came in,
So softly she entered, her feet made no din;
She came close beside me, and this she did say
"It will not be long, love, till our wedding day."

PADRAIC COLUM

RAPUNZEL, RAPUNZEL

Rapunzel, Rapunzel,
Let down your golden hair
As far as to the top step
Of the stone stair,

The stone stair, Rapunzel,
That goes on down forever.
There is no coming up again,
Ever, ever, ever.

Rapunzel, Rapunzel,
Nevertheless I came.
For love of you I climbed it.
Here then I am.

Rapunzel, Rapunzel,
Be kind to me at last.
Let down your long and golden hair—
But haste, Rapunzel, haste!

MARK VAN DOREN

IN WEATHERBURY STOCKS

"I sit here in these stocks,
And Saint-Mary's moans eleven;
The sky is dark and cold:
I would I were in heaven!

"What footsteps do I hear?
Ah, you do not forget,
My Sophy! O, my dear,
We may be happy yet!

"But—. Mother, is't your voice?
You who have come to me?—
It did not cross my thought:
I was thinking it was she."

"She! Foolish simple son!
She says: 'I've finished quite
With him or any one
Put in the stocks to-night.'

"She's gone to Blooms-End dance,
And will not come back yet:
Her new man sees his chance,
And is teaching her to forget.

"Jim, think no other woman
To such a fellow is true
But the mother you have grieved so,
Or cares for one like you!"

THOMAS HARDY

THE GREEN BUSHES

'Twas early one morning in the month of May
To hear the birds whistle and see the lambs for to play.
I heard a young damsel, so sweetly sang she,
Down by the green bushes he thinks to meet me.

I'll bring you fine beavers, a gay silken gown,
And fine silken petticoats flounced to the ground
If you'll forsake him and come on with me
Down by the green bushes where he thinks to meet thee.

O none of your beavers, nor gay silken hose.
Dost thou think me so mean as to marry for clothes?
But if you'll prove constant and loyal to me
I'll forsake the green bushes and follow with thee.

Come let us be going, kind sir, if you please,
Come let us be hasting from under the trees,
For yonder he cometh, so cheerful, so free
For by the green bushes he thinks to meet me.

O when he came there and found she was gone
He looked so distressed and he stood all forlorn.
She is off with another and quite forsook me
So adieu ye green bushes for ever, said he.

I will be as a schoolboy, my time pass in play,
No false hearted maiden shall while me away.
No false hearted maiden shall trick me no more,
So adieu ye green bushes, 'tis time to give o'er.

from *TWELFTH NIGHT*

Come away, come away, death,
  And in sad cypress let me be laid.
Fly away, fly away, breath;
  I am slain by a fair cruel maid.
My shroud of white, stuck all with yew,
        O, prepare it!
My part of death, no one so true
        Did share it.

Not a flower, not a flower sweet,
  On my black coffin let there be strown.
Not a friend, not a friend greet
  My poor corpse, where my bones shall be thrown.
A thousand thousand sighs to save,
        Lay me, O, where
Sad true lover never find my grave,
        To weep there!

WILLIAM SHAKESPEARE

A BALLAD MAKER

Once I loved a maiden fair,
Over the hills and far away,
Lands she had and lovers to spare,
Over the hills and far away.
And I was stooped and troubled sore,
And my face was pale, and the coat I wore
Was thin as my supper the night before
Over the hills and far away.

Once I passed in the Autumn late,
Over the hills and far away,
Her bawn and barn and painted gate,
Over the hills and far away.
She was leaning there in the twilight space,
Sweet sorrow was on her fair young face,
And her wistful eyes were away from the place,
Over the hills and far away.

Maybe she thought as she watched me come,
Over the hills and far away,
With my awkward stride and my face so glum,
Over the hills and far away.
Spite of his stoop, he still is young,
They say he goes the Shee among,
Ballads he makes; I've heard them sung
Over the hills and far away.

She gave me good-night in gentle wise,
Over the hills and far away,
Shyly lifting to mine, dark eyes,
Over the hills and far away.
What could I do but stop and speak,
And she no longer proud, but meek?
She plucked me a rose like her wild-rose cheek—
Over the hills and far away.

To-morrow Mavourneen a sleeveen weds,
Over the hills and far away,
With corn in haggard and cattle in sheds,
Over the hills and far away.
And I who have lost her, the dear, the rare—
Well, I got me this ballad to sing at the fair,
'Twill bring enough money to drown my care,
Over the hills and far away.

PADRAIC COLUM

from CYMBELINE

Fear no more the heat o'th'sun,
　　Nor the furious winter's rages;
Thou thy worldly task hast done,
　　Home art gone and ta'en thy wages.
Golden lads and girls all must,
As chimney-sweepers, come to dust.

Fear no more the frown o'th'great;
　　Thou art past the tyrant's stroke;
Care no more to clothe and eat;
　　To thee the reed is as the oak.
The sceptre, learning, physic, must
All follow this and come to dust.

Fear no more the lightning flash,
　　Nor th'all-dreaded thunder-stone;
Fear not slander, censure rash;
　　Thou hast finished joy and moan.
All lovers young, all lovers must
Consign to thee and come to dust.

No exorciser harm thee!
Nor no witchcraft charm thee!
Ghost unlaid forbear thee!
Nothing ill come near thee!
Quiet consummation have;
And renownéd be thy grave!

WILLIAM SHAKESPEARE

AS I WALKED OUT ONE EVENING

As I walked out one evening,
  Walking down Bristol Street,
The crowds upon the pavement
  Were fields of harvest wheat.

And down by the brimming river
  I heard a lover sing
Under an arch of the railway:
  "Love has no ending.

"I'll love you, dear, I'll love you
  Till China and Africa meet,
And the river jumps over the mountain
  And the salmon sing in the street,

"I'll love you till the ocean
  Is folded and hung up to dry
And the seven stars go squawking
  Like geese about the sky.

"The years shall run like rabbits,
  For in my arms I hold
The Flower of the Ages,
  And the first love of the world."

But all the clocks in the city
  Began to whirr and chime:
"O let not Time deceive you,
  You cannot conquer Time.

"In the burrows of the Nightmare
  Where Justice naked is,
Time watches from the shadow
  And coughs when you would kiss.

"In headaches and in worry
   Vaguely life leaks away,
And Time will have his fancy
   To-morrow or to-day.

"Into many a green valley
   Drifts the appalling snow;
Time breaks the threaded dances
   And the diver's brilliant bow.

"O plunge your hands in water,
   Plunge them in up to the wrist;
Stare, stare in the basin
   And wonder what you've missed.

"The glacier knocks in the cupboard,
   The desert sighs in the bed,
And the crack in the tea-cup opens
   A lane to the land of the dead.

"Where the beggars raffle the banknotes
   And the Giant is enchanting to Jack,
And the Lily-white Boy is a Roarer,
   And Jill goes down on her back.

"O look, look in the mirror,
   O look in your distress;
Life remains a blessing
   Although you cannot bless.

"O stand, stand at the window
    As the tears scald and start;
You shall love your crooked neighbour
    With your crooked heart."

It was late, late in the evening,
    The lovers they were gone;
The clocks had ceased their chiming,
    And the deep river ran on.

INDEXES

INDEX TO AUTHORS

INDEX TO TITLES

INDEX TO FIRST LINES

ह 256

ACKNOWLEDGMENTS

Thanks are due to the following for permission to include copyrighted poems:

American West Publishing Company and Austin and Alta Fife for "The Broken Wedding Ring" from *Ballads of the Great West* by Austin and Alta Fife, copyright © 1970 by the American West Publishing Company, Palo Alto, California.

Bantam Books Inc. for "Springfield Mountain," transcribed from the singing of Bill Bonyun, "The Rich Lady over the Sea," and "Roll, Alabama, Roll" from *Ballad of America: The History of the United States in Song and Story* by John Anthony Scott.

Basil Blackwell Publisher for "Have over the Water to Florida" from *An American Garland* by C. H. Firth.

Brandt & Brandt for "Melora's Song" from *John Brown's Body* by Stephen Vincent Benét, Holt, Rinehart and Winston, Inc. Copyright, 1927, 1928, by Stephen Vincent Benét, Copyright renewed, 1955, 1956, by Rosemary Carr Benét; and lines from *Western Star* by Stephen Vincent Benét, Holt, Rinehart and Winston, Inc. Copyright, 1943 by Rosemary Carr Benét, Copyright renewed © 1970 by Thomas C. Benét, Stephanie B. Mahin, and Rachel Benét Lewis.

Jonathan Cape Ltd., the Executors of the Estate of C. Day-Lewis, and the Hogarth Press for "Is It Far to Go?" from *Collected Poems 1954* by C. Day-Lewis.

Chatto and Windus, Ltd. for "The Dear Girl" from *Time Importuned* by Sylvia Townsend Warner.

S. T. Crawford, Jr. Attorney-in-Fact for: Jean Thomas, The Traipsin' Woman for "Going up the River from Catlettsburg to Pike" and "Working in the Mines, Boys" from *Ballad Makin'*, Copyright 1939 by Jean Thomas, The Traipsin' Woman.

ဆ 263

Edited by Helen Plotz

THOMAS Y. CROWELL CO.

The Earth Is the Lord's:
Poems of the Spirit

Imagination's Other Place:
Poems of Science and Mathematics

Poems from the German

Poems of Emily Dickinson

Poems of Robert Louis Stevenson

Untune the Sky:
Poems of Music and the Dance

The Marvelous Light:
Poets and Poetry

MACMILLAN PUBLISHING CO., INC.

The Pinnacled Tower:
Selected Poems of Thomas Hardy

GREENWILLOW BOOKS

As I Walked Out One Evening:
A Book of Ballads

20953

821.08
AS

As I walked out one
evening

DATE			
DEC 1 0			